CLARINET
SOLO BOOK 1A
REVISED EDITION

Jump Right In
the instrumental series

Richard F. Grunow
Professor of Music Education
Eastman School of Music
of the University of Rochester

Edwin E. Gordon

Christopher D. Azzara
Associate Professor of Music Education
Eastman School of Music
of the University of Rochester

AN INSTRUMENTAL METHOD DESIGNED FOR DEVELOPING AUDIATION SKILLS AND EXECUTIVE SKILLS

INSTRUMENT	BK 1	CD 1	BK1 & CD	BK 2	CD 2	BK2 & CD	SOLO BK 1A	SOLO BK 1B	SOLO BK 2	SOLO BK 3
Flute	J250	J251	J252	J289		J290	J339	J353	J150	J204
Clarinet	J253	J254	J255	J291		J292	J340	J354	J151	J205
Oboe	J256	J257	J258	J293		J294	J341	J355	J152	J206
Bassoon	J259	J260	J261	J295		J296	J342	J356	J153	J207
Alto Sax	J262	J263	J264	J297		J298	J343	J357	J154	J208
Tenor Sax	J265	J266	J267	J299		J300	J344	J358	J155	J209
Trumpet	J268	J269	J270	J301	J316	J302	J345	J359	J156	J210
Horn in F	J271	J272	J273	J303		J304	J346	J360	J157	J211
Trombone	J274	J275	J276	J305		J306	J347	J361	J158	J212
Baritone BC	J277	J278	J279	J307		J308	J348	J362	J159	J213
Baritone TC	J280	J281	J282	J309		J310	J349	J363	J160	J214
Tuba	J283	J284	J285	J311		J312	J350	J364	J161	J215
Percussion	J286	J287	J288	J313		J314	J351	J365	J162	J216
Recorder	J231	J232	J233	J247	J245CD	J245	J94		J149	J217

RECORDED SOLOS WITH ACCOMPANIMENTS

CD/Bk 1A:	Cassette Bk 2:	Cassette Bk 3:
J352	J148	J200
CD/Bk 1B:	CD Bk 2:	CD Bk 3:
J366	J148CD	J200CD

LISTENING

Simple Gifts	*Don Gato*	*You Are My Sunshine*
Cassette:	Cassette:	Cassette:
J229CS	J201CS	J199CS
CD:	CD:	CD:
J229CD	J201CD	J199CD

GIA Publications, Inc., 7404 S. Mason Ave., Chicago, IL 60638

NOTE TO STUDENTS, PARENTS, AND TEACHERS[1]

You may begin using *Solo Book 1A with CD* and also *Solo Book 1B with CD* from *Jump Right In: The Instrumental Series – for Winds and Percussion* when you have learned to audiate and perform many of the songs in *Student Book One*. Exemplary performances and accompaniments for the songs in this book are recorded on the CD included inside the front cover.

Try to perform the songs in this book by ear before performing them from notation. First you should listen to the songs and audiate as they are performed by the professional musician on the CD that accompanies this book. Next, you should sing the songs and learn to perform them by ear on your instrument (A and B listed below – under MUSICAL ENRICHMENT ACTIVITIES).

Notice in the notation that dynamic markings, tempo markings, stylistic markings, and articulations are not indicated. After listening to the professional musician, indicate by marking with a pencil the dynamics, tempos, stylistic markings, and articulation for each solo in the manner that it is performed on the CD. The *Music Theory* section of *Student Book Two* and *Composition Book One* provide information to help mark your music. Mark the notation with a pencil because you may decide to try musical ideas that are different from those used by the professional musician on the recording. Ask your instrumental music teacher for suggestions.

Additional MUSICAL ENRICHMENT ACTIVITIES are listed below for each song. The *Fingering Chart, Slide Position Chart,* or *Keyboard Organization Chart* in the back of this book will help you when locating unfamiliar pitches on your instrument.

You will enjoy performing all the songs in this book with your friends. When performing a few songs, however, you may wish to perform the melody an octave above or below the written melody. In some cases you may wish to perform the melody in a different keyality (start on a different note). At times, you may enjoy just listening to the performances on the CD.

Chord symbols (C, G7, Dm, etc.) are included above the music notation. You may use the chord symbols when learning to perform accompaniments, variations, and improvisations of the songs. Your instrumental music teacher will explain how to use chord symbols.

MUSICAL ENRICHMENT ACTIVITIES

A. Sing the song. You may sing the song in a different keyality (start on a different note) than found on the CD.
B. Perform the song on your instrument by ear in the same tonality and keyality that is on the CD.
C. Perform the song in a second keyality.
D. Perform the song in a third keyality.
E. Perform the song with a friend who plays the same or a different instrument.
F. Perform the song in a different meter. (For example, play duple meter tunes in triple meter and play triple meter tunes in duple meter.)
G. Perform the song in a different tonality. (For example, play major tonality songs in minor tonality, and play minor tonality songs in major tonality.)
H. Perform the bass line for the song.
I. Perform an improvisation or harmony part for the song.
J. Indicate the notation for the song. Ask your instrumental music teacher about *Solo Books – Writing*.

A☐	C☐	E☐	G☐	I☐
B☐	D☐	F☐	H☐	J☐

---

[1] *Solo Book 1A with CD* (50 tunes) *and Solo Book 1B with CD* (50 tunes) from *Jump Right In: The Instrumental Series* were originally released as *Solo Book One* (100 tunes). Solo Books 1A and 1B feature a varied musical repertoire that follows the key sequence of instruction in *Jump Right In: The Instrumental Series – for Winds and Percussion.*

4

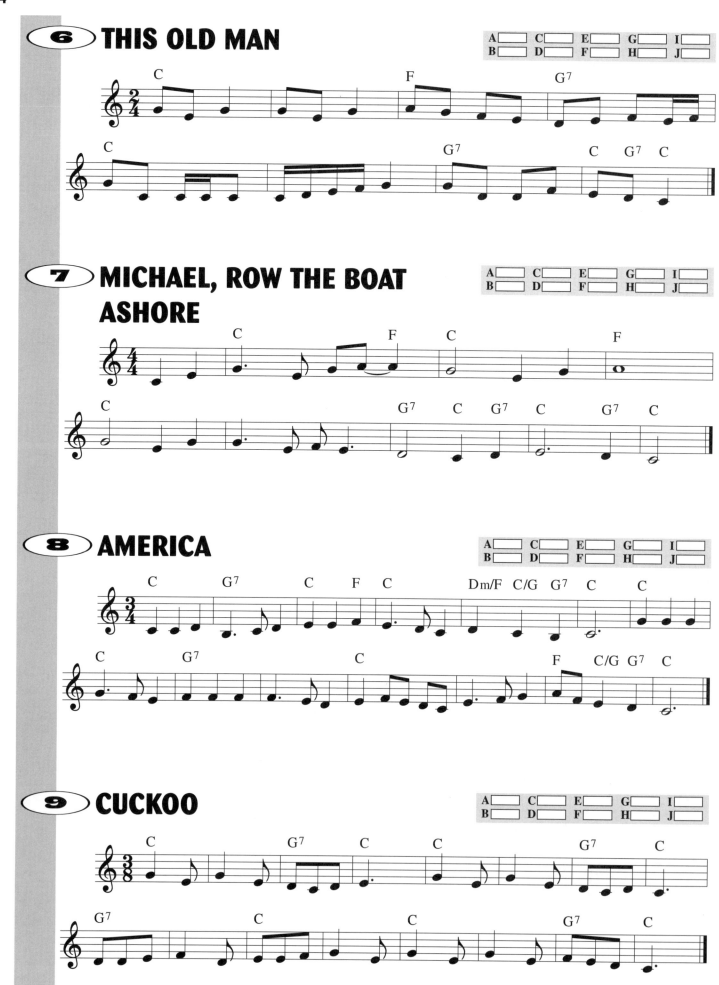

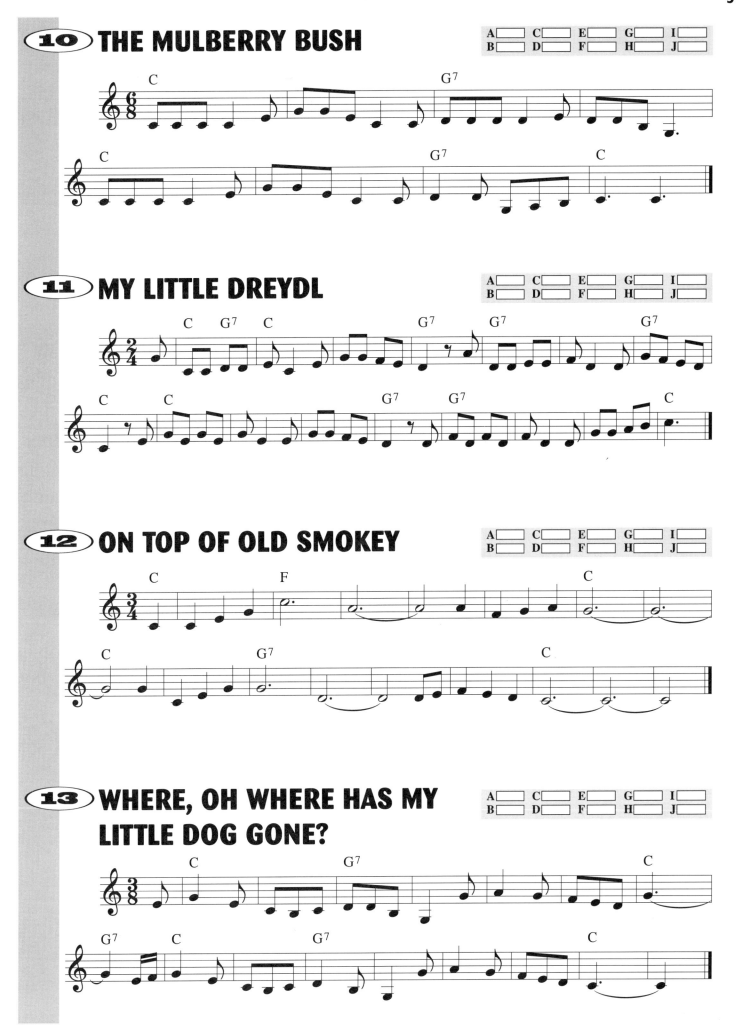

6

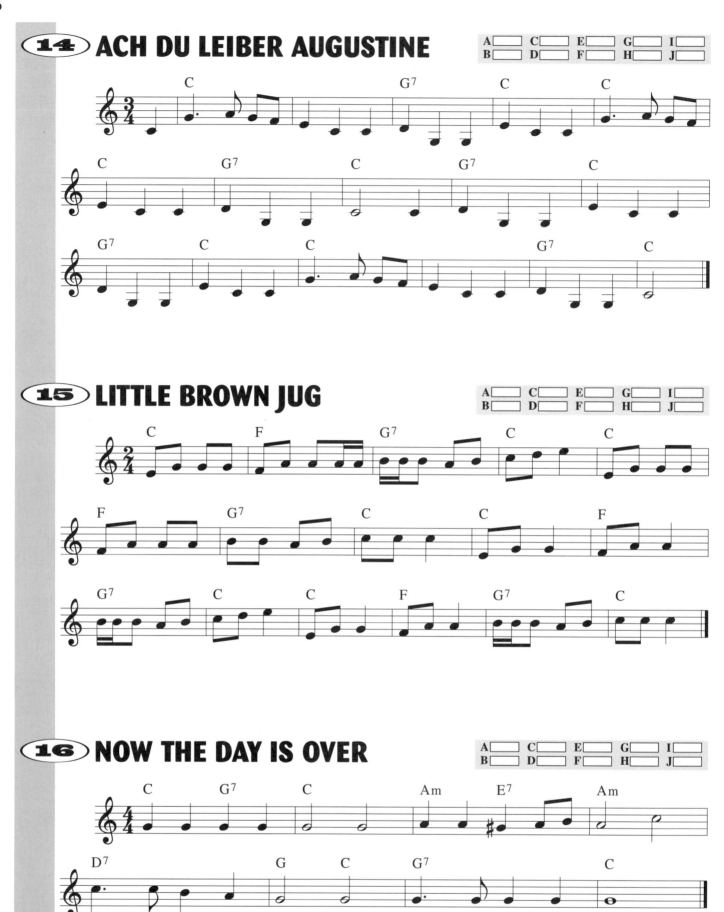

7

17 THREE BLIND MICE

18 RIG A JIG JIG

19 POP, GOES THE WEASEL

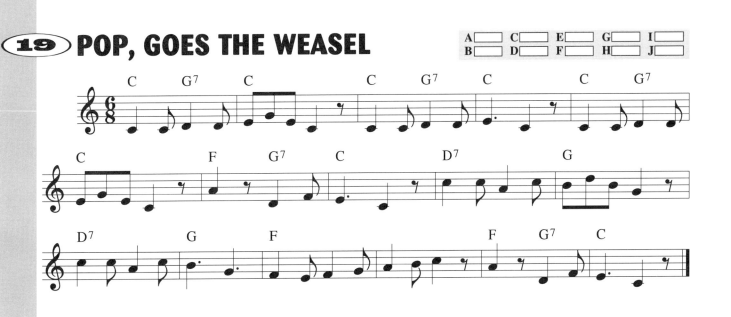

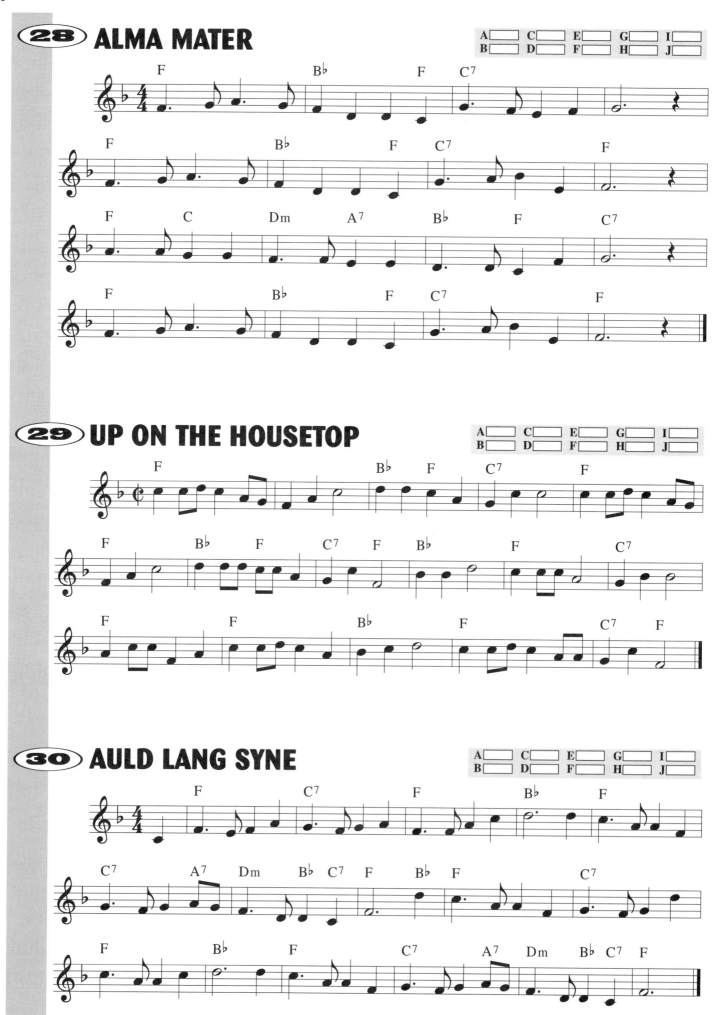

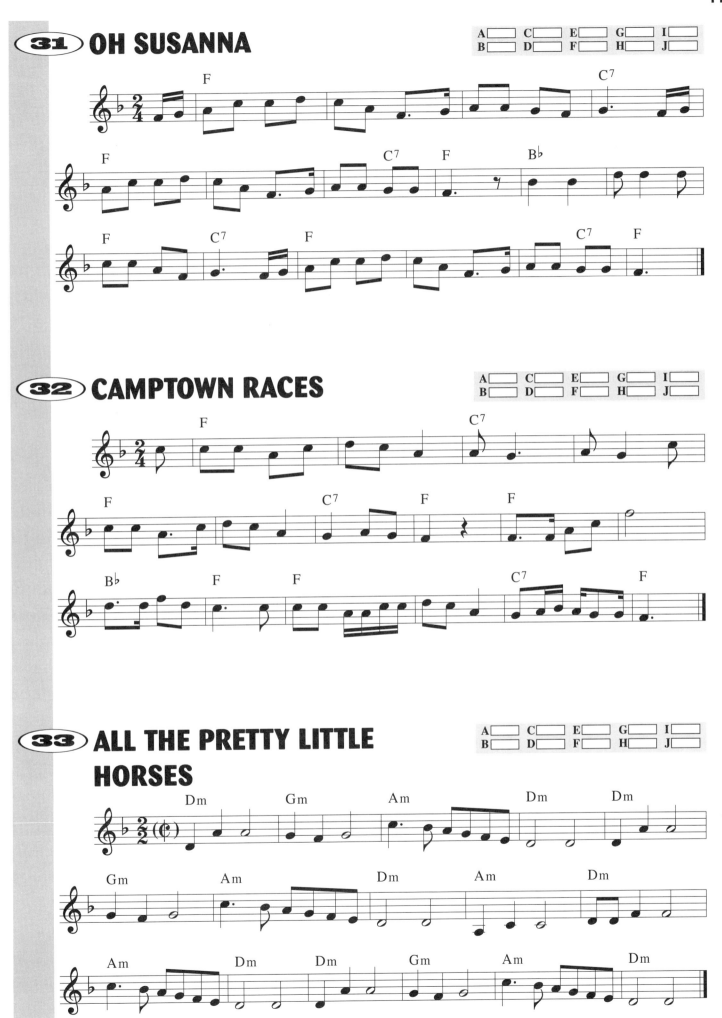

38 MEXICAN HAT DANCE

39 BLOW THE MAN DOWN

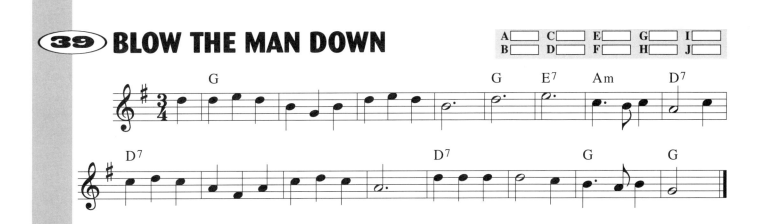

40 JINGLE BELLS

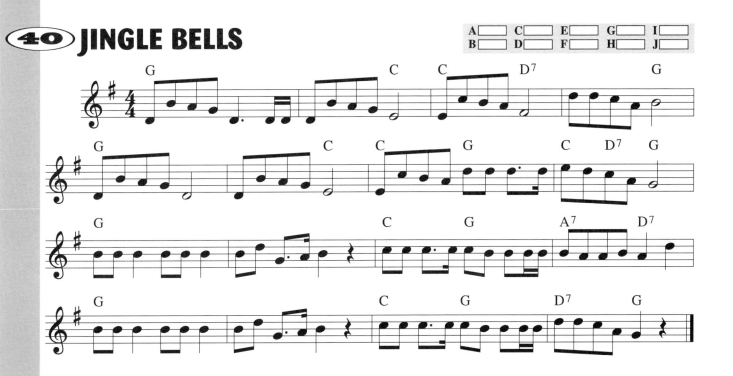

14

41 EENCY, WEENCY SPIDER

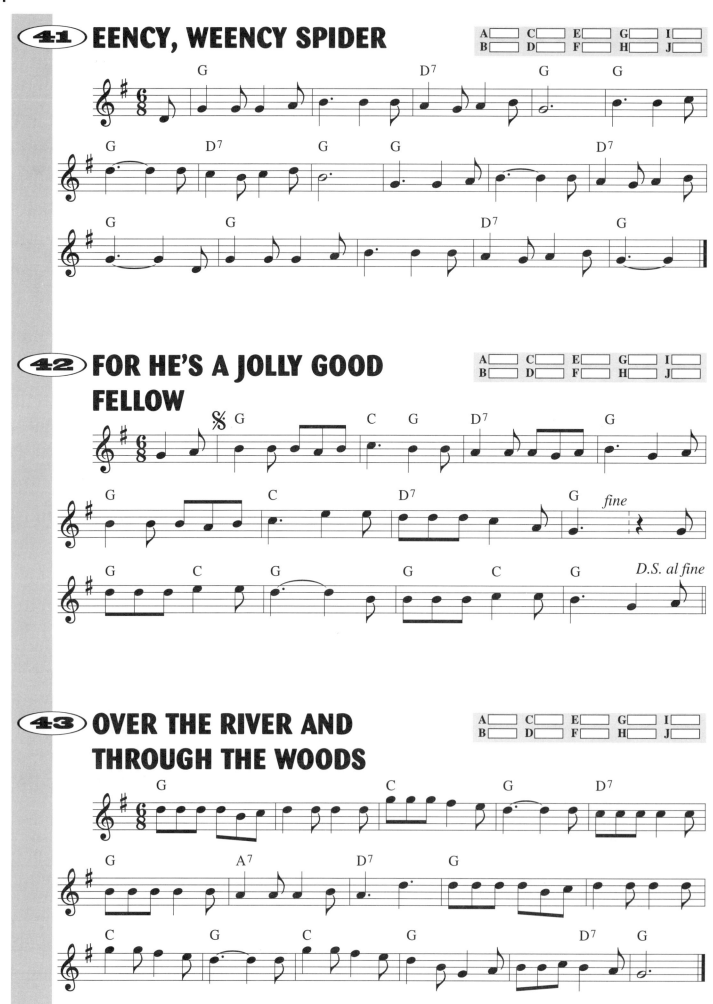

42 FOR HE'S A JOLLY GOOD FELLOW

43 OVER THE RIVER AND THROUGH THE WOODS

15

16

48 JOSHUA

49 SNAKE DANCE

50 SHALOM ALAYCHEM

MW00669144

THE
KITCHEN
STUDIO

THE KITCHEN STUDIO

KITCHEN

CULINARY
CREATIONS BY
ARTISTS

BY MASSIMO BOTTURA

During the course of the last year I have spent a lot of time with my books. With our restaurant closed for months at a time, I was determined to put the book collection in order after years of neglect (there were random piles of books everywhere). Actually, I had a double nightmare—two book collections in two locations. The cookbook collection is in the offices of Osteria Francescana, the restaurant that I have owned and operated for more than 25 years, in Modena, Italy. The art book collection resides in our apartment.

Back at the restaurant, with help from a couple of waiters, two chefs, the reservationists, and our office manager, we took every cookbook off the shelves and cataloged them one by one. We then dusted off the jackets and repaired torn pages before we returned them to newly made bookshelves. At home, we did the same. In a desperate attempt to create order where there was chaos, we designed more bookshelves to contain the books that had taken over our living spaces. Try to imagine this: I am knee-deep in books when the mock-up of *The Kitchen Studio* arrives at my doorstep. My first thought is, "Oh no, not another book!!!" Then I take a closer look.

I have thousands of cookbooks and the truth is I never cook from them. I read the recipes and look at the pictures. I devour them in one sitting and imagine the ingredients and the techniques playing out like dramatic scenes in a novel until I start to get a flavor. When I began to read this cookbook, I couldn't taste anything. Unlike other cookbooks, some of the photography is taken with an iPhone. The food doesn't look like cookbook food. Actually, the food sometimes looks better in the drawings, especially when they are in color. Another thing—the recipe format changes all the time. There are strange diagrams, collages, and poems. There are personal doodles and drawings like diary entries. There are images that look like they have been borrowed from science textbooks, there is eccentric lettering, and some nearly illegible handwriting. At first everything about this book is alarming. And then I got the flavor of it: create.

More than instructions on how to make a cake or a casserole, these recipes are like self-portraits. They are like little windows for spying into the artist's studio. We are invited to look around and be curious about what is happening.

The Kitchen Studio is a visual adventure. It is a gallery of portraits. Certain recipes are comforting and others make me laugh. There is nostalgia and identity, experimentation and irony. There is a Slow Tomato & Cucumber Salad (see page 063), Green Yellow Red: A Colourful Egg Dance (see page 088), The John Cage Omelette (see page 133), and The Wandering in Foggy Morning Mushroom Soup (see page 132) to keep you curious. Food Pigments on Studio Sourdough Bread (see page 082) with vegan butter is about as complicated as a recipe gets and is a wonderful treat for the senses. There are simple cakes and cookies and stews too.

A How to Make Jam recipe (see page 092) and a Jungli Maas curry recipe (see page 104) are ones that can make any home cook shine. I never knew the origins of guacamole (see page 066) nor ever imagined the poetry of two cherries picked from a tree (see page 190). I did not know that you could translate a Kandinsky painting into a taste (see page 058) or that The Brutalist Kitchen had so many rules (see page 126)! I am an Italian chef but I have never heard of a Cacio e Pepe recipe that sounds like a manifesto: three ingredients—no more, no less (see page 136). The Art of Good Taste (see page 176) speaks about food as ritual. And at the end of a hard day, at the office or the studio or the kitchen, how can you not want to make a recipe which beckons you to "Come again to the little kitchen where everything you like still likes you" (see page 134)?

Owning a lot of cookbooks is everyday business for a chef but a mass of art books requires a little more explanation. I've always been an art enthusiast and collector and over the years the art installed at Osteria Francescana has breathed life into our modest-sized restaurant, which has just three dining rooms, an entrance, and a narrow windowless hallway. Maurizio Cattelan's work of embalmed pigeons hanging in the wood beams brought an absurdist point of view into the dining room; Gavin Turk's bronze bin bag sitting in the hallway reminded us of the unwanted trash waiting to be taken out of the kitchen; and when Duane Hanson's 1979 *Security Guard* Frankie glanced at his scuffed shoes because he was tired of standing at the entrance day after day, we felt tired too.

In fact, we found that living and working with art changes us. We were not the same after sitting in a room lined with Carsten Höller's *Birds* or Vik Muniz's photograph of *Pictures of Junk*. One of Ed Templeton's *Teenage Smokers* caught your gaze unexpectedly with their mix of innocence and rebellion and Olafur Eliasson's Icelandic landscapes brought nature to our kitchen cave. As you can imagine, in time, the line between cooking and art became blurred. Art gave wings to ideas that flutter like Damien Hirst butterflies through air thick with the scent of creativity.

So is *The Kitchen Studio* a cookbook or an art book? It is both. Read it like an art book and then cook from it. There are some great recipes in here, and some silly ones too! There are recipes that will make you laugh and recipes that will make you see the world from another point of view. Treasure this book as a means of stepping closer to the creative process of the artists featured in these pages. After devouring it from cover to cover my dilemma is figuring out if it should be shelved with the cookbooks or with the art books. My guess is that I will need two copies.

Massimo Bottura

THE KITCHEN

STUDIO

STUFFED MUSSELS

Serves 6

- 1 kg mussels, cleaned and de-bearded (discard any with cracked shells or any open mussels that don't close when tapped lightly on the work surface)
- 2 glasses of dry white wine
- 2 sprigs rosemary
- 1 bay leaf
- 1 slice of crusty bread
- whole (full-fat) milk, for soaking
- 300 g ripe, firm tomatoes
- 100 g mortadella, minced (ground)
- 50 g canned tuna in oil, drained
- handful grated Parmesan cheese
- 2 eggs, lightly beaten
- 3 cloves garlic, finely chopped
- parsley, finely chopped, to taste
- 2–3 tablespoons extra-virgin olive oil
- root ginger, finely chopped or grated, to taste
- salt and pepper

Put the mussels into a pan with a lid. Add a glass of white wine, the rosemary and bay leaf, cover with the lid and steam over medium heat just until the shells open. Transfer the mussels to a sieve or colander set over a bowl and leave them to drip without dividing the shells. Half-opening them will be enough. Discard any shells that do not open.

To prepare the stuffing, first put the bread into a bowl and cover with milk. Leave to soak, then squeeze the bread dry. Meanwhile, blanch the tomatoes in boiling water, then drain them and run under cold water. Peel away and discard the skins, and finely chop. Mix the mortadella and tuna in another bowl with the bread, the grated cheese and the eggs; season with half the garlic and parsley, salt and pepper to taste and thoroughly combine.

Using a teaspoon, stuff the mussels with the mixture and tie them closed with kitchen twine. Heat the olive oil, the remaining garlic and parsley, and ginger to taste in a large deep pan; pour in the remaining white wine and once it has mostly bubbled away, add the peeled, chopped tomatoes. Cook for 10 minutes, stirring a few times, then add the mussels in a single layer. Cover and continue to cook for 20 minutes before serving.

Opposite page, top to bottom: Philosopher Fabien Vallos presents 'Les Moules et Marcel Broodthaers', salon Jackie, atelier A Constructed World, Paris; Cozze Ripiene, *Parler aux anguilles*, a luncheon with food for eels, with mussels, clams and prawns, salon Jackie, 6 May 2018; Un déjeuner THE SHAKEN: *Parler aux anguilles*, l–r: Angélique Buisson, Fabien Vallos, Max-Louis Raugel, Jacqueline Riva, Claude Richard, Lídia del Rio, Maxime Bichon, Dominique Hammen. Salon Jackie, atelier A Constructed World, Paris, from 13h 30, 6 May 2018.

Left: THE SHAKEN: *Vitrine*, sculpture and archive that was submerged into the Canal de l'Ourcq in Pantin, to be viewed by eels, as part of the performance *Parler aux anguilles*, at the Cneai, les Magasins généraux, 13 June 2018. With works by: Jules Bernagaud, Lídia del Rio, Dominique Hammen, Claude Richard, Louis Pierre-Lacouture, Nina Safainia and A Constructed World. Right: Free swimmer Jérémy Landes (of the Laboratoire des Baignades Urbaines Expérimentales) guides THE SHAKEN: *Vitrine* into the 2.2-metre depth of the Canal de l'Ourcq to be viewed by eels 20h 30, 13 June 2018.

CONFIT LAMB SHOULDER

I rub and massage three 600–700-g shoulders with a mixture of yellow curry powder, fleur de sel, cumin seeds and a good-quality olive oil, made into a paste. I put the lamb into a deep roasting pan and cook it in a 125–160°C (260–320°F) oven for 3–5 hours. The meat is ready when it is tender, well caramelized and is easily pulled off the bone with my fingers.

I find something tart and fresh, like baby plum tomatoes served with olive oil and sumac, goes well with something confit, like the lamb shoulder.

Bon appétit,

Adel Abdessemed

OVERLEAF: *Politics of Drawing, Dionysos, 2020*

L'Epaule d'agneau Confite

Je la frotte et la masse avec du curry jaune, de la fleur de sel des graines de Cumin et de la bonne huile d'olive, je la cuis au four à 160, ou 125 degrés pendant 3 à 5 H . . .
La viande est prête lorsqu'elle est bien caramélisée et que je peux enlever l'os avec mes doigts . . .

bon appetit

Adel Abdessemed

Adel Abdessemed

MAMA'S EGGPLANT SALAD

SERVES 4

3 eggplants (aubergines)
olive oil, to drizzle
3 onions
3 peppers (red, green and
  yellow or just green)
2 cloves garlic, crushed
  (use more or less depending
  on your taste)
chili powder, to taste
  (more if you like it spicy)
vinegar, to taste
ground cumin, to taste
1 bunch fresh parsley
1 bunch fresh cilantro
  (coriander)
salt and pepper

Preheat the oven to 375°F (190°C).

Cut the eggplants (aubergines) into small cubes, put them into a roasting pan, sprinkle with salt, drizzle over some olive oil and mix well. Roast in the oven until tender.

Meanwhile, cut the onions and peppers into small cubes, put them into a separate roasting pan, sprinkle with salt, drizzle over olive oil and mix well. Roast in the oven until tender.

Let the roasted vegetables cool.

Mix all the roasted vegetables together in a bowl, add the garlic, chili powder, vinegar, and cumin, and season with salt and pepper.

Chop the parsley and cilantro (coriander) and mix into the roasted vegetables.

ENJOY

The Carrot Vendor, December, 2018. He sells all different types of carrots as well as some other root vegetables. He is standing in front of my parents' apartment building in Cairo. Each time I go there I think I am traveling in time and not in space.

Nigerian Oha Soup with Fufu made from *Acha* (Fonio)

O24

SERVES 2

INGREDIENTS

8 medium-size *ede ofe* (cocoyams)
1 bunch *oha* (African rosewood) leaves
1 handful *uziza* leaves or a teaspoon
of *uziza* seeds (Ashanti pepper or
Benin pepper)
1 leg of roasted chicken, or raw chicken
2 large *asa* fish (smoked-dried fish)
peppers, to taste (the yellow fresh peppers
locally known as Nsukka peppers are
very nice)
onions, garlic, ginger, salt and ground
pepper, to taste
100 ml of palm oil or palm nut paste
1 teaspoon ground *okpei* (you may also
use *ogiri* or *iru*) seasoning
3 tablespoons of ground crayfish

SOUP PREPARATION

Wash the *ede ofe* (cocoyams) thoroughly with water to remove any dirt. Place in a pot, pour enough water into the pot to cover the *ede ofe*, set over high heat and boil until very tender. Drain, peel off the brown skin and pound the *ede ofe* in a mortar with a pestle (or blend in a blender to get a soft stretchy paste).

Tear the *oha* (African rosewood) leaves by hand and set aside. Slice the *uziza* leaves (or grind the *uziza* seeds) and set aside.

Clean and prepare the chicken (if raw) and fish. Place them in separate pots and steam these separately with the peppers, onions, garlic, ginger and salt to taste. Steam the fish for 10 minutes and set aside. Let the chicken (if raw) boil in its juice for a few minutes, then add some more water when the juice starts to dry up. Steam the chicken for up to 20 minutes – continue to steam until tender. Initially add water to cover the chicken but not enough to completely drown it. Then watch the chicken to ensure it does not dry out and burn.

When the chicken is tender, add the cleaned, dried, steamed fish and boil for 2–5 minutes. Remove them from the stock and set aside.

Add the palm oil or palm nut paste, ground *okpei* (or *ogiri* or *iru*), ground crayfish, ground pepper and *ede ofe* paste to the chicken/fish stock.

Stir well and leave to simmer until the *ede ofe* dissolves and the soup is thickened. You may need to add more water to lighten the soup to your desired consistency, then add the chicken and the fish to the boiling soup.

Add the *uziza* – sliced leaves or ground *uziza* seeds – and boil for about 1 minute. Add the shredded *oha* leaves and turn off the heat. Leave the pot uncovered so the leaves do not get overcooked. Serve hot with fufu made from *acha* (fonio).

ACHA (FONIO) FUFU PREPARATION

Bring 300 ml water to boil in a pot.

Sprinkle in 80 g *acha* (a type of fine grain, similar to millet) while stirring and allow the mixture to cook until a consistent paste is obtained.

Continue cooking while stirring vigorously until you obtain a thick, smooth, homogeneous paste.

Add a little more water, cover the pot and simmer for an additional 8 minutes.

Stir some more – vigorously – until the thick paste is smooth.

Transfer the paste to a dish.

Eat warm, with the soup.

Untitled, 1983–1985

Untitled, 1983–1985

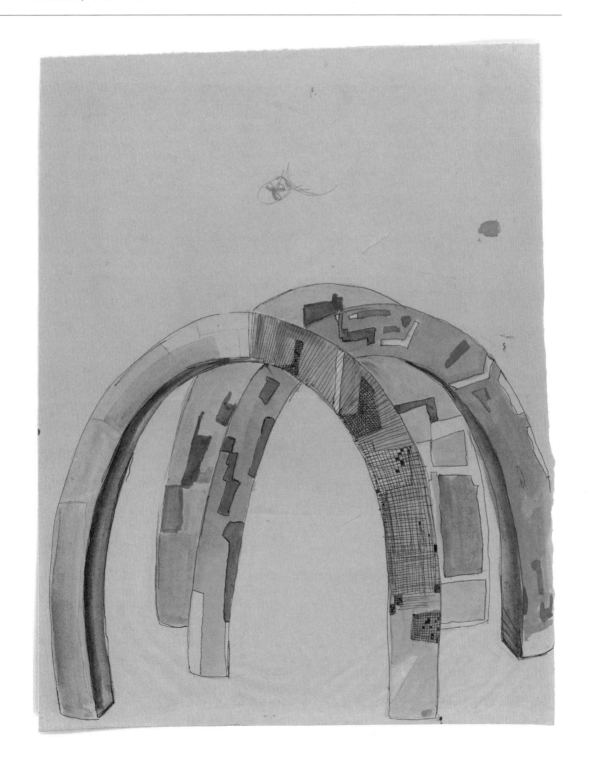

COLD UDON AND MICROCOSMUS SABATIERI

Microcosmus sabatieri are called *foúskes* (pronounced 'foo-skeh-s') in Greek. This edible, stony-shaped sea creature of the Mediterranean is known as a grooved sea squirt in English and, in French, as *figue de mer*, *violet* or *patate de mer*...

In London, being a swimmer usually means swimming in concrete swimming pools, but when you live in a warmer city, like Athens, one with a long friendly coastline, the meditative abstraction of a swimming pool's tiled grid transforms into a wild, cavernous, immensely varied landscape.

Swathes of rock pools that look like noise – irregular, jaggedy and hard to make sense of – or the smooth sand and dense weedy underwater forests of Poseidonia, call for a different pace, and demand looking and searching; after all, foraging for food is a pretty natural instinct.

The more time we spend in Athens, the more my swimming objectives transform. They soon become less horizontal and more vertical. It is extraordinary how easily the body adapts. It's a genetic built-in response: our body responds with bradycardia when immersed in cold water, allowing us to stay oxygenated on a dive.

When you're on a dive, whenever you spot what looks like an anomaly on a rock formation, you feel the urge to prod it; yes, something as formless as a rock has an identity and we automatically perceive anything that breaks this continuity.

With no tide, diving is not a walk on an Essex beach; it's a time-consuming, albeit meditative search, undertaken while fighting against the human body's own fatty buoyancy.

This new obsession of mine seems to tie in with a natural instinct to forage, to look for irregularities, pattern-seeking.

The rewards are endless: rock oysters; Noah's ark *(Arca noae)* the original ancient delicacy before common mussels were farmed; giant Triton's Trumpets (*Charonia tritonis*); and an animal now an endangered species, almost mythical, the giant silk mussel or fan mussel (*Pinna nobilis*); and native seafoods that have almost disappeared as foodstuffs, having little or no user's manual for harvesting or for cooking.

These are mostly molluscs embedded deep in the seabed, forming parts of rocks, camouflaged to disguise themselves in the Mediterranean's waters.

And there they were, the strangest ones: *Microcosmus sabatieri* (*foúskes*).

On close inspection they were slightly exaggerated, cartoon-like even, as though trying too hard to look like the rock they're on. Slightly purpler than grey, with an abundance of surface camouflage. They felt like hard rubber, the same consistency as a tennis ball perhaps.

A memory I couldn't quite recall led me to think these were *foúskes*, the mythical delicacy of the sponge divers from the island of Kalymnos in the deep Aegean. '*Foúskes*' means 'bubbles' in Greek, and they looked like their name suggested. The Mediterranean knows about them; they exist in the Dalmatian, Ionian and Aegean seas.

Foúskes are from the sub-phylum called Tunicates and what is extremely interesting about them is that their structure is biologically related to the human heart. These types of cells, which are traced in the genome of Tunicates, are right at the beginning of an evolutionary path that led to our internal organs, our mammalian heart and its valve system.

Their larval stage is similar to that of a tadpole, with a nervous system, a tail that swims and a brain that chooses a spot to settle on. After this, the animal absorbs its spinal cord and its tail, and becomes simply a siphon of water, motionless and calm.

The taste of *foúskes* is admittedly odd: bursting with iodine, it's briny yet aromatic, with a texture between a Chinese soup dumpling and uncooked prawns (shrimp).

It appears to me – in highly unscientific empirical observation – that the specific quality of the water they live in and siphon affects their individual taste: from the warmer greener waters of the Argosaronic, they are saltier and more pungent, while the clear oligotrophic waters of wind-battered north Aegean have a cleaner taste, and are milder and crisper.

Because of the iodine content, these gems are eaten simply cut open like a fruit and scooped out raw, juices mopped up with bread, perhaps with a splash of lemon as well.

Any heat would instantly reduce the iodine and salt even further and make it too strong, and destroy the delicate flavours. So as far as I have found, no one cooks *foúskes* with heat.

In Kalymnos the only existing semblance of a recipe for *foúskes* is in fact a preservation technique: the flesh is scooped out and enclosed in a bottle filled with sea water, then sealed with wax. The cure from the brine extracts water from the flesh, making it even stronger, like the fermented funk of a lemon confit times 100. This can only be served as a meze to have with a sweet aniseedy drink like ouzo or *tsipouro*, and it is a tradition in the port town of Volos, north of Athens.

Especially today, in light of the urgent need for sustainable foods, perhaps *foúskes* and other indigenous little nutrition/taste bombs are the right direction. They can be grown easily, are super-abundant once one knows how to spot them, and as long as the water they are in is clean, they are free of pollutants.

This simple recipe uses the acidity of the tomato and the lemon to slightly cure the *foúskes* and tame some of the pungency; and in complementary turn, the saltiness of the *foúskes'* brine macerates the tomato, making an almost sweet emulsion to coat the cold pasta.

It is a dish far more sustainable than the popular *uni* (sea urchin) pasta, which effectively abuses the roe of sea urchins; those constitute the bread-and-butter staple for many marine mammals and should not be harvested, especially in the optically clear but nutritionally poor waters of the Mediterranean.

<u>a small dish for two</u>

-- 2–3 lemon-size *foúskes*
-- ½ cup lemon juice
-- grassy olive oil, to taste
-- one beef tomato or a big handful of ripe cherry tomatoes, seeded and chopped into small cubes
-- fresh oregano leaves
-- scant 1 cup udon noodles, fresh or dry, cooked and chilled – you just need the noodles to hold some sauce (you can use linguine if you prefer)

For the dressing:
-- ½ teaspoon cornflour (cornstarch)
-- ½ teaspoon mild mustard powder
-- ¼ cup lemon juice

In a small bowl, whisk the cornflour (cornstarch) and mild mustard powder with the lemon juice to make a dressing.

Halve the *foúskes* on a chopping (cutting) board that has a rim so it catches the juices that will flow, and scoop out the flesh. Be gentle. You can chop each half into two, giving you 4 pieces from each.

<u>Stage 1:</u>
Mix the ½ cup lemon juice, olive oil, *foúskes* flesh and their juices, and the tomato cubes in a bowl and let the mixture sit at room temperature for around 10 minutes. This will macerate the tomatoes and release their juices and infuse the oil.

<u>Stage 2:</u>
Strain the liquid into a separate bowl, and whisk well with the dressing (this acts as a binder and will emulsify the dressing a little). Then add the oregano leaves and the noodles/pasta and toss to coat thoroughly.

Portion the dressed noodles/pasta onto plates, adding the *foúskes* on top.

A RECIPE IN TWO PARTS

Part One
You need around 2 kg of terracotta clay and a kiln.

You form an 8-cm (3-inch) wide sheet of clay by rolling out the wet clay. Once it is a little drier, dry enough to hold its shape, you kneel and you fold and mould the clay over your horizontal thigh to form a curved tile.

Wait a little so the tile holds its shape. This is best done in a sunny setting for speed. Let it dry, supporting its shape with something underneath, then fire it in the kiln until it is dry and hard.

Part Two
You need a bonito, mackerel, kingfish or small tuna small enough to fit inside the tile.

You roast the fish on the tile over a medium flame or in an oven set to 180°C/350°F. A 500-g fish would need about 20 minutes. Add 5 minutes for every additional 200 g of fish. The tile will absorb the fish's fat and evenly disperse it. The tile forms a micro-oven, which keeps the flesh moist and the temperature even all the way around. The tile absorbs the fat and bastes the fish while it cooks. The tile is then discarded.

One of the unique elements of the cooking process is the amount of labour and energy that goes into preparation, and the resulting sense of 'present-moment' enjoyment when people come together to dine.

Tasting food is an intensely present-moment experience and perhaps this is one of its stress-relieving effects.

The contrast of discarding a ceramic tile somehow intensifies the importance of eating a whole animal, in a way honouring its sacrifice.

The anthropomorphous shape of the tile is important. This is how tiles were always made in antiquity, the craftsman's knee giving Roman tiles their shape.

This recipe is a fictional adaption of one I found in my grandmother Maria's hand-drawn cookbook, which she left for my mother. I never got to meet her in person, but this 'recipe' generated so much in my imagination as a child.

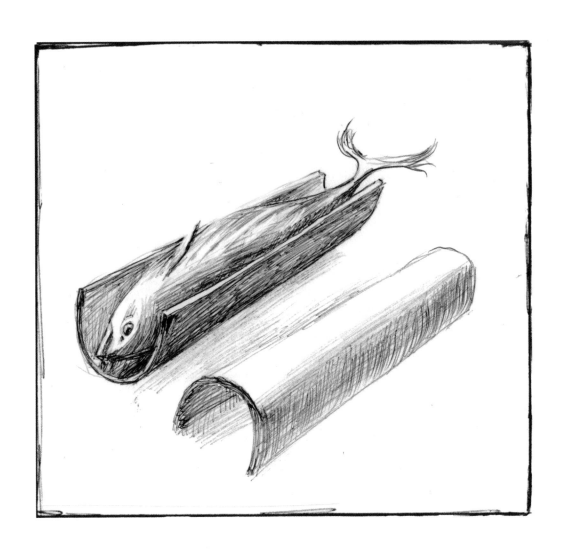

ATHANASIOS ARGIANAS

COLD UDON AND MICROCOSMUS SABATIERI /
BONITO ON A ROOF TILE

LEGENDARY ABSINTHE
OF PROFESSOR NARRO

INGREDIENT LIST

* One 70 cl bottle of any type of clear spirit with an alcohol content of at least 50 per cent alcohol by volume (ABV). Possible options are white rum, grain alcohol, mezcal or vodka (the chosen alcohol type MUST HAVE 50 per cent ABV OR MORE, otherwise the ingredients will not release their properties sufficiently).

* 200 g finely chopped fresh or pre-dried wormwood leaves (*Artemisia absinthium*). Ideally, the dried leaves should be ground in a mortar with a pestle on the same day that the absinthe production begins.

* 150 g hyssop (*Hyssopus officinalis*). We use the whole plant (leaves and stems) ground in a mortar with a pestle on the same day that the absinthe production begins.

* 10 g star anise (*Illicium verum*)

* 30 g aniseed (*Pimpinella anisum*)

* 20 g fennel seeds (*Foeniculum vulgare*)

* 6 g lemon balm (*Melissa officinalis*). We use the whole plant (leaves and stems).

* 3.2 g coriander seeds (*Coriandrum sativum*)

* 1.8 g sweet flag or calamus root (*Acorus calamus*)

For the second maceration, all or some of the following plants may be used, depending on personal preference (see notes about fresh and dried and fresh herbs on page 034). The combinations are endless. These are merely my suggestions as a huge variety of plants and seeds can be used. The process of discovering and creating new flavours and personal versions of absinthe is what makes it so much fun.

* Heath speedwell (*Veronica officinalis*)

* Cardamom (*Elettaria cardamomum*)

* Thyme (*Thymus vulgaris*)

* Lavender (*Lavandula angustifolia*)

* Mint (any plant from the *Mentha genus*)

* Hibiscus (*Hibiscus rosa-sinensis*)

* Chamomile (*Matricaria recutita*)

* Garden angelica root (*Angelica archangelica*)

* Basil (*Ocimum basilicum*)

* Rosemary (*Salvia rosmarinus*)

* Cinnamon sticks

* Vanilla pods

* Nutmeg

* Sage (*Salvia officinalis*)

If none of these plants are available, as a last resort the contents of an infusion or tea bag made of these plants may be used. Nothing beats fresh plants, but infusion bags may well come to the rescue.

Absinthe must always contain the 'Holy Trinity' of herbs: wormwood, aniseed and fennel.

Use one standard US measuring cup (250 ml) of herbs and seeds, or less, per 70 cl of alcohol.

Wash your hands, your work surface, and your herbs. Chop, shred or grind the ingredients (see notes below). Wormwood may be chopped or shredded (if you can't grind it). You can use a pestle and mortar to grind seeds such as aniseed. Plants and seeds release their properties more efficiently when ground or finely chopped.

Place the prepared ingredients into freshly sterilized sealable storage jars or glass preserving jars of similar sizes and pour in the alcohol to top off.

Seal the jars and store in a dark, warm place for a period between two weeks and two months to allow the 'Holy Trinity' and other herbs to fully infuse the alcohol. This process is known as maceration, and its duration will directly affect the flavour. If macerated for too long, it will become bitter and murky; too little, and it will lack flavour. Anything over two months or under two weeks is not advisable. It is important to check how the maceration process is progressing.

Once the mix turns a pleasant colour and develops an intense flavour, it needs to be strained. Strain the mix and the herbs through a piece of clean muslin (cheesecloth), a coffee filter or similar. The resulting liquid will most likely look brown or murky green and have a bitter taste. After straining, you can taste the liquid to assess the bitterness and then proceed to the second maceration of herbs and seeds. This second maceration will bring out the absinthe's true colour and flavour.

For the second maceration, use a lot less wormwood – ideally as little as possible – to minimize the bitter taste. This is when you should add the plants for the second maceration and any herbs you wish to use. This is the fun bit, where you can get creative and come up with different versions. This second maceration is very important because it determines the depth of colour and flavour – add any flavours you want to enjoy. Allow the mix to macerate to taste, but no longer than one month so you do not end up with a mix that is too bitter.

At the end of the double maceration process, you will be ready for the final stage. Strain the liquid again to prepare it for the final mixing process.

The mixing process is highly important: you need to combine the mix with your favourite clear spirit in order to dilute it – either with vodka, mezcal, gin or any distilled clear spirit of your choice. Mix it, taste it, then continue to mix as necessary. Too much alcohol (spirit), and the liquid will burn like a strong liqueur. Too much of the macerated mix, and the drink will become too bitter. It is important to find the right balance, but that is a matter of personal taste. The absinthe can also be sweetened at this point, with anything from sugar, to sugar substitutes such as corn syrup, honey or agave nectar.

If you wish to use *panela* (unrefined whole cane sugar obtained from evaporated sugarcane juice) in solid form, half a block (about 100 g) will do, but it is best to add it to the second maceration and not to the final mix.

Bottle the drink, label it, invite your colleagues, friends and family over and enjoy it in any way you choose.

Be sure to source good wormwood leaves and dry them yourself. Alternatively, you can use them fresh, if preferred.

Do not try to speed up the process. Patience is key for good absinthe.

Always use fresh and clean ingredients and prepare everything in a clean environment. That said, herbs are normally dried before use. If you wish to use them fresh, it is important to chop or grind them well.

Do not use large quantities of star anise, nutmeg, sage or wormwood, as they can be toxic if consumed to excess.

Do not use more than one standard US measuring cup (250 ml) of herbs for every 70 cl of alcohol used to infuse them, to avoid ending up with excessively bitter absinthe.

I recommend making several litres of the first maceration, then play around with different combinations in the second maceration to find your personal signature.

Never stop experimenting.
The possibilities are endless!!!

EL CABALLO DE TURÍN

* * * * * * * * * * * * * * * * * * *

Makes 1 cocktail

Ingredients:
4 large ice cubes
2 fl oz of mezcal
1 fl oz of white vermouth
1 fl oz of rosemary-infused simple
    sugar syrup
2 fl oz of unsweetened *agua de jamaica*
    (hibiscus tea—prepare slightly
    beforehand)
juice of ½ a lime
rosemary sprig, to garnish

1. Place one ice cube in a cocktail
   shaker.
2. Pour the mezcal, the vermouth, the
   rosemary syrup, the hibiscus tea,
   and the lime juice into the shaker.
3. Close tightly and shake well.
4. Pour over a glass filled with the
   remaining ice cubes and garnish
   with a rosemary sprig.

"In Turin on January 3, 1889,
Friedrich Nietzsche steps out of the
door of Number Six Via Carlo Alberto,
perhaps to take a stroll, perhaps
to go by the post office to collect
his mail. Not far from him, or indeed
very removed from him, a cabman is
having trouble with his stubborn
horse. Despite all his urging, the
horse refuses to move, whereupon
the cabman – Giuseppe? Carlo? Ettore?
– loses his patience and takes his
whip to it.

Nietzsche comes up to the throng
and that puts an end to the brutal
scene of the cabman, who by this time
is foaming with rage. The solidly
built and full-moustached Nietzsche
suddenly jumps up to the cab and
throws his arms around the horse's
neck, sobbing. His neighbour takes
him home, where he lies still and
silent for two days on a divan, until
he mutters the obligatory last words:
'*Mutter, ich bin dumm*', and lives
for another ten years, gentle and
demented, in the care of his mother
and sisters.

Of the horse ... we know nothing."

From *A torinói ló* (*The Turin Horse*).
Directors: Béla Tarr and Ágnes
Hranitzky, 2011
Screenplay writers: Béla Tarr and
László Krasznahorkai

While it may be a commonly held belief that milk chocolate is an inferior product compared to dark chocolate, milk chocolate can also be made with single-origin cacao beans, and with the same refinement and precision as the most sophisticated dark chocolate for the so-called 'chocolate connoisseurs'.

Indeed, just because the industry has tended to pervert milk chocolate by mixing low-quality cacao beans together, using palm oil and soya lecithin (rather than cacao butter), vanillin and cheap milk powder, and drowning the whole mix in an overdose of sugar to lower production costs, does not mean that milk chocolate cannot be an extremely sophisticated product.

This is therefore a recipe for a dark milk chocolate bar (55 per cent cacao), coating and smoothing in the mouth and with just sufficient sugar to please the general public as well as single-origin chocolate connoisseurs.

It is actually interesting and amusing to note that this milk chocolate is 1 per cent stronger in single-origin cacao than one of the dark-chocolate flagships of the Belgian industry.

THE RECIPE

Preparation for 100 kg
of chocolate / 1,667 bars
of 60 g each

· organic cacao nibs (37 kg), which
  will require about 45 kg of raw
  cacao beans before the winnowing process
· organic cacao butter: 18 kg
· organic milk powder: 33 kg
· organic sugar: 12 kg

Take the raw cacao beans, ideally of organic origin. I recommend the beans from the Marañón plantation in Peru, or the beans from the hills of Idukki in Kerala, India.

Even though the beans will have been already fermented and dried on site after the harvest, and even though the fermentation kills part of the germ, you will need to roast the beans.

Prior to the roasting, the beans need to be carefully sorted and cleaned of the various debris or stones found in the bags.

After the beans have been properly cleaned, put them in the oven for 30 minutes at 120°C (250°F). This roasting operation will kill all possible remaining bacteria and will increase the cacao aroma.

After roasting, the beans must be cracked and winnowed in the cacao winnowing machine, thus separating the shell from the nibs.

The cacao nibs can now be ground in a pre-grinding machine before undergoing a finer grinding.

At the end of the pre-grinding step, the nibs should reduce to a thick paste with a mean particle size of around 100 microns.

The finer grinding should then start and its refining process will reduce the particle size of the chocolate paste to an average of 20 microns.

At this point you can start adding, step by step, the cacao butter, then the milk powder, and continue grinding.

As soon as the chocolate paste is homogeneous again you can add the sugar.

You are now starting the conching process, which should last for at least 48 hours with regular heat airflow during the process.

This conching step will determine the finesse of the flavour and the smoothness of the consistency of the finished chocolate.

When the chocolate is sufficiently ground, you can start the tempering process in the tempering machine.

Since we are producing milk chocolate, the temperature should first reach 50°C (120°F), then be reduced to, and stabilize between 28°C and 29°C (82°F and 84°F).

At this stage, the chocolate is ready for moulding and should be placed in a refrigerator for 20 minutes maximum at around 9°C (48°F). Do not leave the chocolate in the refrigerator for too long or it will start accumulating condensation, which will damage the chocolate.

Your Pierre Bismuth's Milk Chocolate Bar is now ready and, even though milk chocolate cannot be stored as long as dark chocolate, it is important to remember that several weeks of ageing will allow the finished chocolate to develop a better, more rounded flavour.

The first Pierre Bismuth's Milk Chocolate Bar was produced in Belgium in 2019 by JAP/Jeunesse et arts plastiques as a limited signed art edition of 100 copies. Its fabrication was realized by the artisanal chocolate manufacturer MIKE&BECKY Brussels.

idt. cola

idt. cola is wildcrafted from an open-source recipe reverse-engineered from the original cola, merging the domestic with the scientific. The cola flavour was created by Cube-Cola and released under the GNU General Public License.

'idt.' is the abbreviation for The Interdependence, a new multi-local alliance between community economies actors, and is an alternative to more familiar identifiers such as ltd or Inc.

The Interdependence exists to make visible and to support people, groups, initiatives and organisations who perceive themselves as interdependent with others, and part of a larger movement to create economies that have the well-being of people and the planet at their core.

idt. cola is made by many:

Cube-Cola (Standing on the Hands of Giants) is hand-manufactured at the Cube Cinema in Bristol (UK) by the unincorporated partnership of Kayle Brandon and Kate Rich.

BAD Cola is made by Company Drinks in Barking and Dagenham (UK), a community drinks enterprise set up by artist Kathrin Böhm, where drinks are made for and with each other.

Ciacola is made by Comunità Frizzante under the slogan 'making drinks to make community' and is based in Vallagarina Valley in the Italian Alps.

ingredients:

Carbonated Water
Sugar
Caramel
Colour E150d
Citric Acid
Gum Arabic
Caffeine
Essential oils: Orange, Lime, Lemon, Nutmeg, Cassia, Coriander, Lavender

I can't remember recipes

I remember ingredients

to
chop
mix
cook
eat.drink

Fake Japanese Breakfast

I am an early bird, at least for the last few years. This might have to do with the simple fact of getting older, or just that my life has become more monotonous. I am afraid both are the case, and I am not complaining. Most days I get up at six-thirty, climb out of bed and amble to the kitchen. There I turn on the wall-mounted coffee machine. After the first sip of coffee, I start laying the ground for my upcoming breakfast operation. Which is a kind of Japanese breakfast. My wife Makiko, who is Japanese, claims my breakfast has nothing to do with a real Japanese breakfast, and I agree with her 100 per cent. My Swiss origins forced me to become a bread-and-butter-eating human being who had his first sushi at 30. But over time, I think I have incorporated some parts of Japanese cooking into my daily morning routine.

Before I begin, I turn my iPhone to landscape mode and start watching the news to get a hold of things out there in the world, something I would simply miss here in the middle of the forest. I believe that, if we did not have access to the Internet, the world could go sideways, and we would not notice it for a while. This fact encourages me even more to watch the news each morning, just to check if the rest of the world is still going.

Back to the breakfast. It contains a piece of marinated salmon served with white rice. A miso soup with about 15 different vegetables, plus tofu (bean curd). A cabbage-cucumber-carrot salad. And sautéed vegetables in a pan, sometimes with an egg in it. Lately I use more eggs since we've had an egg flood here in Upstate New York; many of our friends bought chickens when the Coronavirus crisis started. To prepare all of this takes about an hour and two cups of coffee. After I am done, I wake up Makiko and my daughter Aka, and we all eat together. At the end of our breakfast, we end the whole thing with a bowl of yogurt and blueberries, and sometimes I give it a final flourish with a piece of chocolate.

I am not hungry until noon. I know it sounds like a lot of food, but it is relatively light on the stomach. And you can eat crap the rest of the day if you want; you got all your good nutrition already in the morning. Of course, we do not do that; we eat three full meals a day in our household. We don't fuck around with food.

OK, now a few words to the images surrounding this text. Several years ago, I joined Instagram because all of my friends were on it. I did not want to be a creep and just follow without posting, so I thought faces are a neutral space to not overexpose my privacy. In retrospect, it was a noble thought, but as we know, often good intentions have nothing to do with reality. After a few years, I guess people who follow me on Instagram know what I am eating each day. Most of the Insta-faces became food faces discovered while cooking.

From the beginning of joining Instagram, I told myself I would never want to become a social media monkey. So I try not to force myself to find new faces. They appear whenever they do – could be today, could be tomorrow, or never. One thing is for sure – the Swiss-Japanese breakfast will be on the menu long after Instagram is gone.

Mrs Onion

Mr Smallguy   Mr Upsidedown   Mr Yoda

Mrs Useful   Mrs Tomatotimeagain   Mrs Stain

Mrs Salmonmouth   Mrs Saladfoot   Mrs Riceskull

Mr Angrymiso

Mrs Crymeariver

Mr Eatmeordie

Mrs Havetogotothedentist

Mrs Coffefaceagain

Mr Forehead

Mrs Needssomeyoga

Mrs Bigbrain

Mr Friendly

FOOD FOR THOUGHT

1 pound unsalted butter, plus extra for greasing
1½ pounds brown sugar
1½ pounds all-purpose (plain) flour
2 teaspoons freshly grated nutmeg
1 teaspoon ground cloves
2 teaspoons ground cinnamon
1 teaspoon baking soda (bicarbonate of soda)
1 tablespoon baking powder
3 pounds raisins
3 pounds currants
1 pound candied (glacé) cherries
1 pound candied citron, sliced
1 pound stoned dates, sliced
½ pound crystallized ginger, sliced
¼ cup almonds, plus extra to decorate
10 eggs, well beaten
1 cup molasses
1 cup strong cold coffee
- juice and grated rind of 2 oranges
- grated zest and juice of 1 lemon
1 cup tart jelly (jam), such as blackberry
- good cognac, brandy or rum, to 'feed' the cake at your discretion. Too much is better than not enough.

Line 2 extra-deep, round cake pans (10 × 3½ inches/25 × 9 cm) with greased parchment (baking) paper, allowing 2 inches (5 cm) of paper to rise above the pans.

Preheat the oven to 300°F (150°C).

Cream the butter and sugar in a large mixing bowl until fluffy.

Sift all the dry ingredients into a separate large mixing bowl

3 times, then add the dried and candied fruit, ginger, and almonds and mix well.

Add the eggs to the creamed butter and sugar mixture and mix gently.

Add the flour-fruit mixture to the butter-sugar mixture alternately with the next 5 ingredients and mix thoroughly (the batter should be very stiff).

Spoon the batter into the prepared pans and decorate the tops with extra almonds.

Cover the cakes with circles of greased parchment paper and bake in the preheated oven for 3–4 hours.

Remove the paper lids for the last half-hour to dry the surface of the cakes.

When a skewer inserted into the center of the cakes comes out clean, the cakes are ready.

Let the cake pans cool on a rack, so that air can circulate underneath.

While still warm, using a skewer, puncture the surface of the cakes all over and pour over some cognac, brandy or rum.

When cool, remove the cakes from their pans. Wrap separately in waxed paper and then in foil and store in a cool place, or in the freezer. Allow the cakes to age for at least 3 months before consuming.

The cakes may be unwrapped annually, or as desired, and more alcohol added, allowing them to last for several years.

My mother baked this cake from 1948 through 1999, when she was 90 years old and the batter was too stiff for her to stir. She has passed her records and her cookbook on to me, and this is the result.

My mother was a British war bride. She came to Canada immediately before the end of the war, depth charges detonating around her, along with a convoy of other boats, also full of British war brides. They came to this country, leaving behind them their culture, their histories, their family and possessions—they were allowed only two suitcases each—and became a defining part of the immigrant population that makes up Canada.

Once I met a Caribbean man from Grenada. He told me of his own traditional family cake and, on tasting mine, pronounced them practically identical. His family cake is made in layers, as a wedding cake, and the different layers are saved for different events of family history—for example the smallest top layer is saved for the christening of the first child.

This is a cake that will keep for years, and survive both time and unfriendly circumstance. It is a medieval recipe that has traveled to the trenches in both World Wars and, like some exotic cultural virus, has reached the furthest corners of the British Empire, and outlasted it as well.

Opposite: Me at the age of four with my mother, Kathleen Alice Tims, in Kensington Gardens, London 1950.

When the bread speaks, my hands follow

Bread in English, *pâine* in Romanian, *pain* in French and *pane* in Italian ...

I have many favourite food recipes from Italy, Romania, France, Japan, India, Thailand, etc, but when it comes to essentials, only one thing comes to my mind: bread. This humble food, which has traversed human history from antiquity to the present day, has taken on the shape and flavour of the times and of the people who have produced it. From basic staple to sacred food, bread is a constant, showing us that there is a chain of interdependence joining the grain of wheat, the fertility of the earth, the human agricultural societal organization and the toil of those who bake it.

I don't want to enter the vast symbolism of bread, but I would mention one that is part of our European heritage and which is part also of my childhood memory: hospitality. When a guest or a stranger approached the home, they were always welcomed with bread and salt.

During the Covid-19 shutdown in spring MMXX, while staying at home my wife started to grow homemade yeast. I had never made bread before. But the moment I touched the flour and the yeast, brought together into dough, my hands recalled the memory of seeing my grandmother making bread hundreds of times, every Saturday of my childhood in the Romanian countryside. I tried to revive those memories, to see what would come from my hands at this first encounter with a substance that was sticking so strongly to my fingers. I tried to create little symbolic pieces that recalled the motifs I might have seen on traditional Romanian blouses worn by farmers in my grandma's village, or the sacred motifs that decorated the surface of the bread made on the occasion of funerals or Orthodox Easter. And this is what came out: a zoomorphic circle, a hashtag-shape, a roped cross, two DNA helix shapes, an anthropomorphic figure and a weaved plain circle. After all, what remains is the beauty of this atemporal process and the price we pay to get it with our time. The rest is pixels.

Mircea Cantor
4 XI 2020
Paris

WHEN THE BREAD SPEAKS, MY HANDS FOLLOW

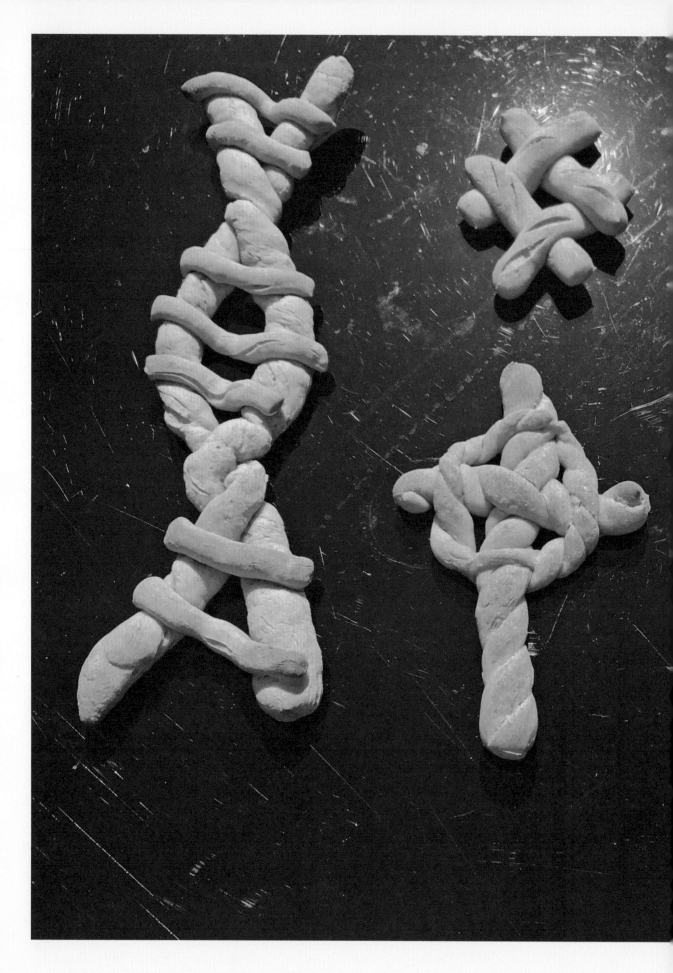

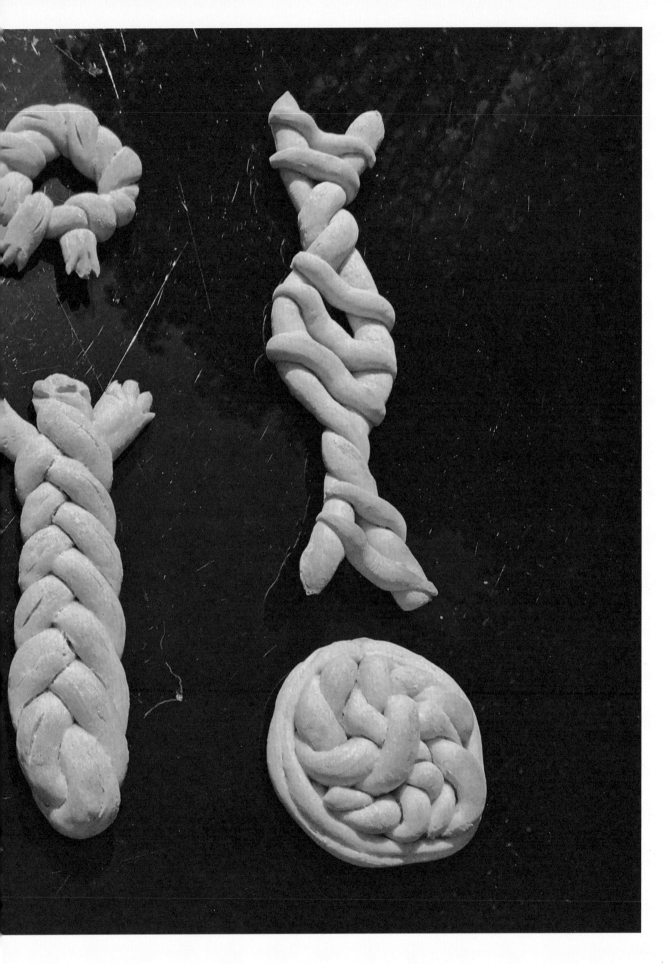

The Physical Experience
of the Metaphysical World

"Sweet is by convention, bitter is by convention, hot is by convention, cold is by convention, color is by convention; in truth there are only atoms and the void."
—Democritus
From *Something Deeply Hidden* by Sean Carroll

As we all know, the void doesn't mean empty space or nothingness. It is void because it represents the perfect balance. What is the perfect balance made of? The answer is, billions of possible states of consciousness.

Paintings are definitely the visual results of our consciousness, and so are tastes. If tastes are governed by convention, and if I know the proper ways to give new orders to tastes, I can develop brand-new tastes, just like creating new images.

Taste could be an exceptional tool that could allow us to travel the unknown world if we were able to expand the world of tastes to the metaphysical, conceptual realm. It could represent the true meaning of psychedelic experience. Using the 64 codes that I have discovered through my analysis of paintings, those analytical elements of paintings can be converted into tastes, not to mention various other forms (senses) such as music and so on.

I chose five paintings by different artists to create five dishes and presented a food exhibition with a brilliant chef, Leo Kang, who could understand the meaning of this project in detail.

Overleaf are the two dishes that I'd like to share, converted from paintings by Pablo Picasso and Wassily Kandinsky.

Psychedelic Knot, 2020. 297 x 210 mm (11¾ x 8¼ inches), digital medium.

The recipe of *Les Demoiselles d'Avignon* by Pablo Picasso, 1907

The definition of this painting's taste is the artificial flavors with five dissolved basic tastes (sweet, salty, bitter, sour, and spicy) in the form of powder.

INGREDIENTS

Corn chips, beef jerky, rice powder, a pinch of salt (salty), sugar (sweet), *yuja* (yuzu) peel (sour), juice squeezed from red ginseng roots (bitter), and capsaicin powder (spicy).

THE PROCESS OF PRODUCTION

We ground corn chips and beef jerky into a rough powder. Then we steamed the rice powder until it turned into a flaky and powdery state. Next, we mixed this steamed rice powder with the ingredients representing the five basic tastes. Then we mixed this with the corn chip and beef jerky powder. We prepared a small cup to give the mixed powder a round shape, and then put it into a bowl and pressed it hard. Lastly, we carefully placed it onto a flat dish while keeping its round shape.

We presented the food and informed guests that they could taste Picasso's *Les Demoiselles d'Avignon* by simply breaking the food with their spoon and eating it.

Les Demoiselles d'Avignon by Pablo Picasso (1907) turned out to be a powdery food. The corn chips and beef jerky provided the artificial flavor we intended to express, and the rice powder had its role to soothe and dissolve the five basic tastes. The analytically shattered flat space shown in this painting was transformed into taste, exhibiting its powdery state.

Some people were hesitant to try the food because the powdery shape reminded them of some sort of condiment or seasoning. Yet others who understood the concept were open to exploring this unfamiliar form of food and even enjoyed it, saying that it would go well with wine.

The recipe of Kandinsky's first painting (*Untitled*), 1910

The definition of this painting's taste is that there are independent boundaries of ambiguous, complex, and specific textures.

In this painting, there are no objects to name or recognize, such as man, tree, a square, or a circle, but what's there are the anonymous lines and brushstrokes. Therefore, this painting has to have a taste of nothingness. What we had to achieve was to produce a food that provides the taste of nothingness, but also the combination of subtleness that comes from ambiguous forms and unorganized structure. It was the most challenging task since every ingredient has its own flavors and tastes.

INGREDIENTS
Abalone, shrimp (prawns), seaweed branches, lotus roots, Japanese mountain yams (*Dioscorea japonica*), a few cabbage leaves, crushed pine nuts, thinly sliced radish, and garbanzo beans (chickpeas).

THE PROCESS OF PRODUCTION:
To create the taste of nothingness, we had to remove all the clues that are recognizable to us from the food material. First, we needed to take all the flavors and saltiness out of these materials. To do so, we soaked them in water and left them for a couple of hours until there were no flavors or tastes left, only the textures. That was also the decoded result from the painting by Kandinsky. We prepared raw and steamed ingredients. Some were ground (minced) and mixed together with the yams, which acted like glue. What was left out was just the state of textures so that we could only taste the boundaries of various textures, and the combination of them. What we can taste then is only the boundaries of various states of textures and it turned out the presentation of an anonymous shape of brushstrokes. This is what Kandinsky's painting tastes like.

I was a bit worried about this Kandinsky course because there were only subtle flavors and tastes left. Yet, to my surprise, it was the dish people loved most, and it got a lot of compliments. Maybe because the dish looked most like the painting, or perhaps people liked its pure taste. This strange food, which was hard to take into our mouths, became a special new taste when it connected to the meaning.

When you give a meaning to a food, even the strangest food that you have ever experienced, it could be the delicacy of your mind.

Claudia Comte's Slow Tomato & Cucumber salad

1

In April, take the seeds from a tomato and place them in a small container filled with potting soil.

2

Water the seeds every three days.

3

In June, move the plant into your garden. Shelter partially—tomatoes grow best in tomato houses, where they are sheltered on three sides. Sometimes it can be better to grow tomatoes in pots rather than in the ground to protect them from animals. If you are planting in the ground layer the soil with stinging nettles, then a layer of soil and plant your tomato plant on top. Planting this way is believed to create a good, sturdy foundation for your plant.

4

Plant using supporting stakes next to them so that the plant has some support to grow with.

5

Remove some of the leaves to ensure the plant gets more sun.

6

Water the plant on a regular basis, but gauge this on the weather, whether it rains or is sunny.

7

In August, harvest the fruit.

8

Take some of your tomatoes and cucumbers* from the garden, wash them, chop, and drizzle with olive oil and aceto balsamico. Add feta cheese.

*The same process applies to cucumbers But the supporting stakes are not necessary!

RECIPE TO REMOVE FARMED SALMON FROM AN ART INSTITUTION

COOKING SECTIONS, SALMON: A RED HERRING

Salmon is the colour of a wild fish that is neither wild, nor fish, nor even salmon.

Salmon was once considered a luxury food but now more than one million salmon meals are eaten in the UK every day. To meet the large consumer demand, intensive salmon farming has expanded to satiate our appetite for this once-wild fish. In salmon farms, hundreds of thousands of salmon at a time are raised in pens suspended in the sea. These large-scale farms present extreme problems for the coastal aquacultures in which they are placed. Thousands of tonnes of waste escaping the nets pollute the surrounding waters. Diseases run rampant.

Salmon is usually thought of as 'salmon pink'. The flesh of farmed fish ought to be grey, but synthetic pigments added to the salmon feed turn the flesh the desired salmon colour that we expect.

Farmed salmon are fed food containing pigments, sometimes chosen by means of the SalmoFan™, a range of fifteen shades of salmon pink. The SalmoFan™ colour measurement scale by DSM is recognized as the industry standard across the world for measuring salmon fillet colour.

The artificially-induced colouring reflects human desire for recognizably 'natural' colours. Salmon is the colour of a wild fish that is neither wild, nor fish, nor even salmon.

The changing colours of species around the planet signal an environmental crisis, and salmon is just one of many colour oddities resulting from the metabolization of manmade substances in human and animal bodies.

Intensive salmon farming produces an excess of nitrogen – which is not the case with filter-feeders such as oysters and mussels, which help to clean water through their breathing and eating. In addition to being crucial agents in removing pollutants from coastal seawater, these creatures provide a good source of protein without the need for feed or antibiotics.

This is the basis of CLIMAVORE, which explores how to eat as humans change climates. Initiated by Cooking Sections in 2015, this long-term project includes a variety of site-responsive iterations that propose adaptive forms of eating in the face of the climate crisis. A form of devouring that responds and cares for food landscapes affected by extractive practices. Different from carnivore, omnivore, locavore, vegetarian or vegan diets, it is not so much the ingredients that define CLIMAVORE, but rather the infrastructural responses to the new human-induced seasons we are living in.

As part of the *Salmon: A Red Herring* project, Tate Britain has removed farmed salmon from its menus across the UK, and introduced a series of CLIMAVORE dishes in their menus.

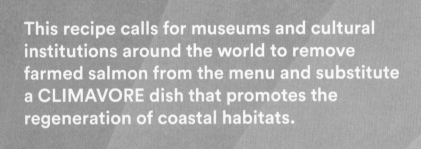

This recipe calls for museums and cultural institutions around the world to remove farmed salmon from the menu and substitute a **CLIMAVORE** dish that promotes the regeneration of coastal habitats.

Salmon is the colour of a wild fish that is neither wild, nor fish, nor even salmon.

GUACAMOLE

"Guacamole" is a bastardized word, a result of colonialism. In Náhuatl, the language of the Aztec people, who built a wide-ranging empire in Central America, the word "*molli*" means "sauce," which was combined with the Náhuatl word "*ahuacaquahuitl,*" which means "testicle."

From *ahuacaquahuitl*, the word designating the fruit, in Spanish it became phonetically *aguacate*. It then traveled to other languages, again phonetically, as *avocat*, avocado, etc. Paleontological evidence shows that the *aguacate* dates back 10,000 years, as is the case with corn. Both are found in the center of the country that we know nowadays as Mexico, or at least what remains of it...

Hass is the most common cultivar, patented by an American farmer bearing that same last name, in the 1930s. Its worldwide consumption and production, which carries deforestation and economic implications, makes the avocado the fourth-most important tropical fruit globally in the twenty-first century. The state in Mexico (one of the largest exporters of avocados in the world) where the most avocados are produced is Michoacán, where my father's family is from. In the local P'urépecha language, aguacate's name is "*cupanda*." Its botanical name is *Persea americana*.

Guacamole has as many versions, although almost all of them include the same ingredients, all of which definitely should be native to the American continent —but of course some add spices *ad libitum*. And obviously there should be no guacamole police denouncing one recipe or another as "fake." Mine is the simplest, easiest, and tastiest... Enjoy.

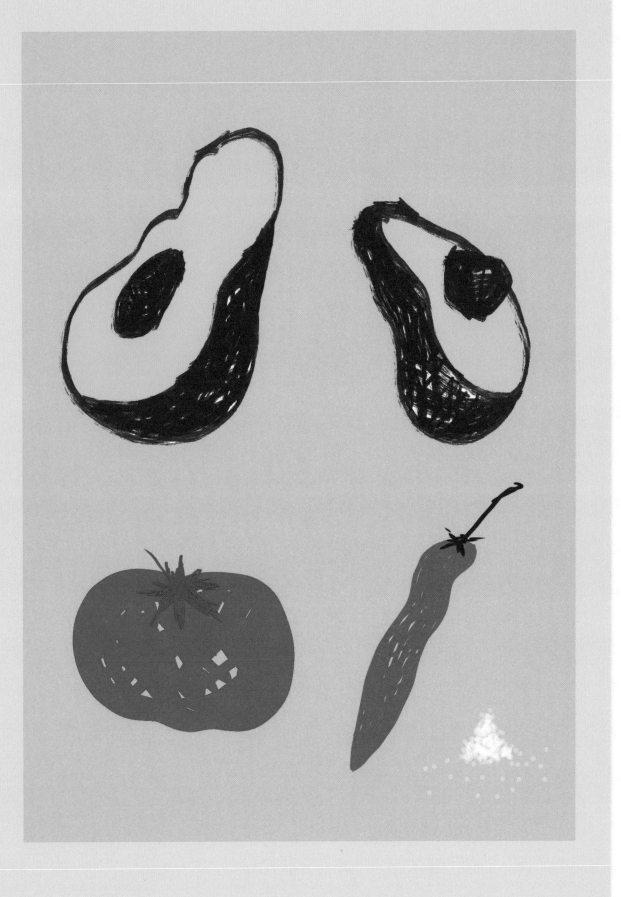

GUACAMOLE
Serves 4

INGREDIENTS
4 aguacates (avocados/*Persea americana*/
  Hass), fist-size and ripe but not soft
1 green serrano chile pepper (*Capsicum
  annuum*)
2 round red tomatoes, fist-size (*Solanum
  lycopersicum*)
1 pinch of salt

OPTIONAL
1 green lime (*Citrus aurantifolia*)
½ white onion (*Allium cepa*)
cilantro (coriander) leaves (*Coriandrum
  sativum*), to taste
blue corn tortilla chips, pork cracklings,
  or potato chips (crisps), to serve

TOOLS
1 knife
1 spoon
1 bowl
1 cutting (chopping) board

Wash your hands the best you can: check your nails and in between your fingers; your main tool should be the neatest they can be, as for caressing your loved one.

Cut each *aguacate* in half and remove the seeds, but don't discard them. Using the spoon, scratch or shave out from each shell all the green avocado pulp, putting it all in the bowl. Discard the shells.

Cut the chile pepper into tiny thin dice, then wash your hands immediately, and don't touch your eyes, face, or any part of your body.

Cut the tomatoes into medium-size dice, *brunoise*, *macédoine* or *mirepoix*, it's up to you...

Put all the cut ingredients, together with the *aguacate* shavings, into the bowl and, with your hands, tightly squeeze the largest pieces to make a homogeneous, but not liquid, mixture. Your fingertips will tell you when it's done.

The result should be a creamy—again NOT LIQUID—consistency that can hold your spoon vertical in the center of the bowl. Texture is also very important, along with smell and flavor, for a real gourmand.

Add salt cautiously. Add the avocado seeds to the mixture, so they hide inside there. They say it helps guacamole to stay green as it prevents oxidation.

Also—both for flavor and maybe for keeping a good color and texture—you can add green lime juice. Squeeze it by hand and mix in.

Onion can be a good companion, but it's not mandatory for this recipe. I would be discreet in general with the use of this bulb. It can kill other flavors and be difficult for digestion, like chile pepper. If you exaggerate, it can become a waste.

Cilantro (coriander) leaves mixed with the final sauce can be good, or use them as a garnish. They're good when tossed as a final touch, with a celebratory confetti gesture...

Guacamole is a side dish, to start a good meal with; it's never a main dish. You can receive friends at home, and while waiting for other invitees, you can share a good guacamole with a little sip of your favorite bubbles, including beer, of course, dipping into the creamy starter with tortilla chips, but much better if you find a way to get pork crackling...

Et voilà.

Note: if you find the way to have access to a volcanic rock mortar (Mexican *molcajete*), you can change the procedure by grinding first salt and chile in it. Then you add avocado as described, then tomato, etc... This doesn't change the flavors much, but it's fun...

I hope you enjoy this, and I would love it if this can be the starting chain of an exchange of pleasure and joy in these times of anxiety and desperate hopelessness... Share it with your friends, if you want, just please remember to write down my name.

Bon appétit,
ac

Chicken in the Oven
with Sumac and Okra in Tomato Sauce

Serves 2

It's a dish I like to make for lunch and dinner for friends, and for myself. I like it because it's cheap (basically chicken with potatoes) and it's special because of the okra. There's no story behind this dish. I started to cook it a couple of years ago after finding a batch of okra in the supermarket, and rediscovering my love for chicken thighs.

- 2 onions
- 2 chicken thighs
- 1 tablespoon garlic powder
- 1 tablespoon sumac
- 1 garlic head, halved
- 2 potatoes
- 1–2 tablespoons vegetable oil
- 12 okra
- 2 tomatoes, chopped
- salt and pepper

(In the photos I used asparagus instead of okra, but I cut it in the shape and the size of okra to get closer to the original idea. I boiled the asparagus together with the potatoes in hot water and later with tomato sauce.)

Chicken

Preheat the oven to 375°F (190°C).

Julienne (thinly slice) 1 onion. Take the chicken thighs, rub them with salt, pepper, garlic powder, and sumac. Place the sliced onion and halved head of garlic on parchment (baking) paper or silver foil and place the chicken thighs on top. Cook it in the oven for 40 minutes.

Okra in tomato sauce

Meanwhile, peel the potatoes, and cut them into slices not thicker than ½ inch (1 cm). Bring a small pan of water to the boil, add the potato slices and boil them for 10 minutes, then drain.

Chop the remaining onion. Heat the oil in a large pan (use one with a lid) over medium heat. Add the chopped onion and fry for 7 minutes. Add the okra and the boiled potato slices and cook for 10 minutes. Add the chopped tomatoes, let it boil, lower the heat and cover the pan with the lid. Let it cook until the chicken in the oven is ready, or for at least for 15 minutes.

Serve the chicken on top of the onion with the side dish of okra and potatoes beside it.

071

CHICKEN IN THE OVEN WITH SUMAC AND OKRA IN TOMATO SAUCE

BORN DAWN DEDEAUX 1952; LONNIE HOLLEY 1950 : LIVE ATLANTA, USA; NEW ORLEANS, USA

MOTHERSHIP & MOTHER UNI-
VERSE'S FLYING GREEN GUMBO

MOTHERSHIP AND MOTHER UNIVERSE'S FLYING GREEN GUMBO (CHICKEN AND ANDOUILLE GUMBO WITH MUSTARD GREENS)

Serves 12-15

Yes, there are a whole bunch of steps involved in making this thick, hearty gumbo, but none of it is difficult. Day one, you make the chicken stock. Day two, you make the roux and put together the gumbo. And then, like most soups and stews, gumbo is best after it's had a chance to sit overnight. Day three is feasting day! Serve with white or brown rice and a sprinkle of filé powder.

The stock
1 x 3-4 lb chicken
4 green onions or scallions (spring onions), chopped
2 yellow or white onions, chopped
3 cloves garlic, chopped
3 carrots, chopped
3 stalks celery, chopped
2 tablespoons chopped fresh thyme or 2 teaspoons dried and crumbled
½ lemon with seeds removed
3 dried chilies (we like Japones or árbol)
garlic power, to taste
salt and cayenne pepper, to taste

The roux
1 cup vegetable oil
1 cup all-purpose (plain) flour, sifted
2 onions, chopped
3 stalks celery, chopped
salt and freshly ground black pepper

The gumbo
1½ -2 lb andouille sausage (we prefer andouille from a supplier called The Best Stop Supermarket just west of Lafayette, Louisiana, who does mail order), cut into ¼-inch (5-mm) pieces
about ½ cup red wine
Worcestershire sauce, to taste
red wine vinegar, to taste
handful fresh thyme, tied into a bundle with butcher twine or culinary string
generous grinding black pepper and cayenne pepper to taste
sea salt
about 1 lb mustard greens and/or kale or baby kale or collard greens, torn into small pieces, stems removed
6 green onions or scallions (spring onions), chopped
½ cup fresh parsley, chopped

Method:

Make the stock: place the chicken, green onions or scallions (spring onions), onions, garlic, carrots, celery, thyme, lemon, and chilies in a large stock pot. Add enough water to almost cover the chicken; there should be 2–3 inches (5–7.5 cm) of space below the rim. Bring to a boil; reduce the heat to medium-low and simmer for several hours until the stock is flavorful. Taste for seasoning and add salt or pepper if needed. If the stock tastes weak, simmer for another 1–2 hours. Remove from the heat, bring to room temperature, and refrigerate overnight.

Remove the stock from the refrigerator the following day and, using a slotted spoon, remove the chicken. Separate the meat from the bones and remove the skin from the meat. Chop the dark meat into about ½-inch (1-cm) pieces and cut the breast meat into slightly larger pieces, then set aside.

Strain the stock into a pot; discard the vegetables and heat the stock over medium-low heat. Taste for seasoning and add salt, garlic powder, and cayenne pepper to taste. Keep the stock over low heat while you make the roux.

Make the roux: You want to make a very dark roux; this is one of the secrets to making great gumbo. Heat the oil in a large skillet or frying pan (preferably cast iron) over high heat for 1–2 minutes. Slowly whisk in the sifted flour, stirring constantly. Reduce the heat slightly if the roux appears to be burning. Cook, stirring, for 10–12 minutes or until it is a dark color. Remove from the heat and immediately stir in the onions, celery, salt, and pepper. This will stop the roux from further burning. Slowly whisk in 1 cup of the prepared stock, whisking until smooth. Add another cup of stock, again whisking until the mixture is smooth. Slowly whisk the roux mixture into the simmering stock, whisking until fully incorporated.

In another large skillet, sauté the sausage until golden brown. Drain off the fat. Add the sausage, wine, Worcestershire sauce, red wine vinegar and thyme to the pot of simmering stock, adding black pepper and cayenne to taste. Simmer over low heat until the gumbo is thickened and flavorful. About 20 minutes before serving, add the greens, green onions, parsley, and reserved cooked chicken meat. Cook until the greens are tender, and the gumbo is fully flavored. Serve hot, with white or brown rice and a sprinkle of filé powder.

GRAPE PIE

- -

This is a recipe from southern Italy
but the grapes are a variety native to
North America. In Italy they are called
uva fragola, strawberry grapes, and were
introduced to Italy in the 1800s. In the
United States they are usually called fox
grapes, I suppose because foxes like them.
But I do too, and so do possums, raccoons—
almost everybody. Back home we called
them muskydimes. The white variety are
called scuppernongs.

- -

- -

These grapes are the origin of American
Concord grapes, which are usually made
into jelly (jam). The taste is intense—
both sweet and sharp.

- -

For this recipe, preheat the oven to 180°C (350°F). Take some almond butter and some almond meal (ground almonds). I do not measure ingredients when cooking, but maybe ½ cup of almond butter and 1 cup of almond meal. Mix them together in a bowl with a spoonful of yogurt and 3 spoonfuls of buckwheat flour.

- -

The mixture should be thick like pizza
dough—though not so elastic, of course.
Spread the dough evenly into a greased
20-cm (8-inch) pie pan up to the rim,
about 1 cm (½ inch) thick. Cover this
with whole grapes, gently pressed into
the dough. Sprinkle the grapes with brown
sugar and bake in the oven for 30 minutes.

- -

Jimmie Durham, 2020, Napoli

ESTABLISHED 1997 : BASED BERLIN, GERMANY

COLOUR ON BREAD

We have a great and dedicated kitchen team at Studio Olafur Eliasson, who have long championed climate-conscious work. Their fresh produce is delivered from Apfeltraum, a community-supported agriculture farm just outside Berlin. For some of the events that we have held in recent years, like for the launch of Mary Robinson's great book *Climate Justice*, the kitchen team put together carbon-neutral dinners. There was a report not long ago entitled 'Food in the Anthropocene', in which the authors advocate a Great Food Transformation to achieve healthy diets for the growing world population and respond to climate change. Our kitchen has already adopted this approach. They are also involved in experiments that bring excitement to the studio work, such as turning vegetables into pigments for a new series of ecologically infused watercolours. I really believe in these larger systems of interconnectivity.

— Olafur Eliasson

FOOD PIGMENTS

As the team working in the kitchen of Studio Olafur Eliasson, we began our pigment project with the intention of wasting as little as possible, by using each and every part of the seasonal produce we receive. We began to put aside peels of onions, beetroot (beet), carrots, parsnips, apples, some of the greens of the leeks, the outer leaves of radicchio, red cabbage, Tuscan kale (cavolo nero), celery leaves, and the scrapings and seeds of pumpkin. While in summer months, it's possible to lay out a linen cloth and dry fruit and vegetable peels and herbs in the sunshine, in winter we use a dehydrator to dry the various ingredients, then use a blender to pulverize them, and a mortar and pestle, where necessary, to create a finer pigment.

The resulting pigments reach beyond the kitchen, forming part of the studio's push towards achieving sustainability in all areas of our practice. The pigments have been used to create watercolours and were featured in the studio's Sustainability Lab as part of Olafur's exhibition *Sometimes the river is the bridge* at the Museum of Contemporary Art Tokyo in 2020.

With our freshly baked sourdough bread and some salted vegan butter, these food pigments make for a beautiful and delicious accompaniment.

— Christine Bopp, Lauren Maurer, Montse Torredà Martí, Nora Wulff

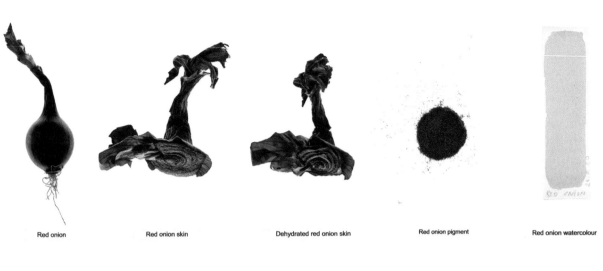

Red onion

Red onion skin

Dehydrated red onion skin

Red onion pigment

Red onion watercolour

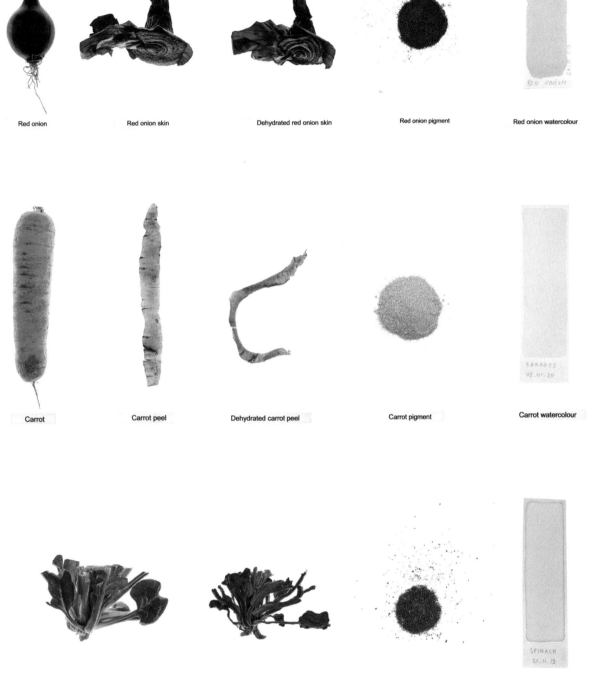

Carrot

Carrot peel

Dehydrated carrot peel

Carrot pigment

Carrot watercolour

Spinach stem

Dehydrated spinach stem

Spinach pigment

Spinach watercolour

VEGAN BUTTER

Makes about 400 ml

240 ml cocoa butter or mild/refined coconut oil
  (for a neutral taste)
120 ml sunflower or other neutral-tasting oil
60 ml plant milk, such as almond, oat, rice
½–1 teaspoon salt

Warm the cocoa butter or coconut oil in a sauce-pan over low heat just until it melts. Whisk in the other ingredients, transfer to a mixing bowl, then put in the fridge for 10–15 minutes until cooled. Using a hand-held mixer, whip until the mixture reaches the desired consistency (it should reach a light and fluffy stage after 2–3 minutes). Place in an airtight container and store in the fridge for up to 2 weeks or in the freezer for up to 3 months.

STUDIO SOURDOUGH BREAD

Makes 1 loaf, plus extra sourdough starter

DAY 1
50 g of your starter (your 'old' sourdough);
  alternatively, you can buy a starter kit
  or ready-made sourdough starter
100 g rye flour
100 ml warm water

Feed your sourdough (if using homemade sourdough): in a bowl, mix the starter with the flour and water. The idea is to make enough for the recipe while keeping some aside as your starter for next time.

Divide the resulting dough into two portions: 100 g and 150 g. Use the 100-g portion for the recipe and let it rise in a bowl covered with a clean dish towel at room temperature for approximately 12 hours (maybe less in the summer and more in the winter). Put the remaining 150-g portion into a jar with a lid. Both portions should double in size. Use the 100-g portion for baking the next day. Keep the 150-g portion in the jar in the fridge for next time.

DAY 2
100 g risen sourdough
500 g strong white bread flour
125 g wholegrain spelt flour
400 ml lukewarm water
18 g salt

1 x proving basket or sieve for the overnight rise
1 x 5-litre ovenproof pot with a lid, for baking

Mix all the ingredients in a large bowl for about 8 minutes. Cover your bowl with an airtight lid and let it rest for 90 minutes. After 90 minutes, it's time to begin folding the dough. At this stage, you will work in the bowl. Dip your hands in warm water, grab the underside of the dough, stretch it and fold it back over itself. Rotate your bowl one-quarter turn and repeat 3–4 times. Repeat this every 30 minutes, 3 times.

Flour your work counter. Now take the dough out of your bowl: slip a spatula under the dough and flip it onto the floured counter. Pull the bottom of the dough up to fold into one third of the round. Pull each side and fold over the centre to elongate the dough vertically. Fold the top down to the centre and then fold the bottom up over the top fold-down, leaving the seam underneath. Let the dough rest for a few minutes, seam-side down, so that the seam seals.

Roll the dough into a ball, turn and put it upside-down in a well-floured proving basket (or in a sieve lined with a clean, well-floured dish towel).

Overnight, keeping the dough in the basket, let the dough rest in the fridge.

DAY 3
Preheat the oven to 250°C (480°F). Place your ovenproof pot (with the lid on) in the oven to heat and, when fully heated, carefully place the pot on a heat-proof surface, take the lid off, carefully flip your bread upside-down into the pot and cut your signature into the dough using the tip of a sharp knife (to allow the bread to rise properly).

Put the lid back on and place the pot in the oven. Bake for 45 minutes. Remove the lid and let the bread bake for another 10 minutes. If you keep the high temperature, the crust will turn dark brown. If you lower the heat a bit, the crust will be lighter.

Take your bread out of the oven, remove it from the pot right away and place it on a cooling rack.

To serve
Either sprinkle the food pigments (see page 082) onto the buttered bread or dip the buttered bread into the pigment. If you like, add salt to taste.

Note: We use biodynamic ingredients. Make sure your ingredients are organic and come from a credible source guaranteeing the peels are free from pesticides and chemical treatments.

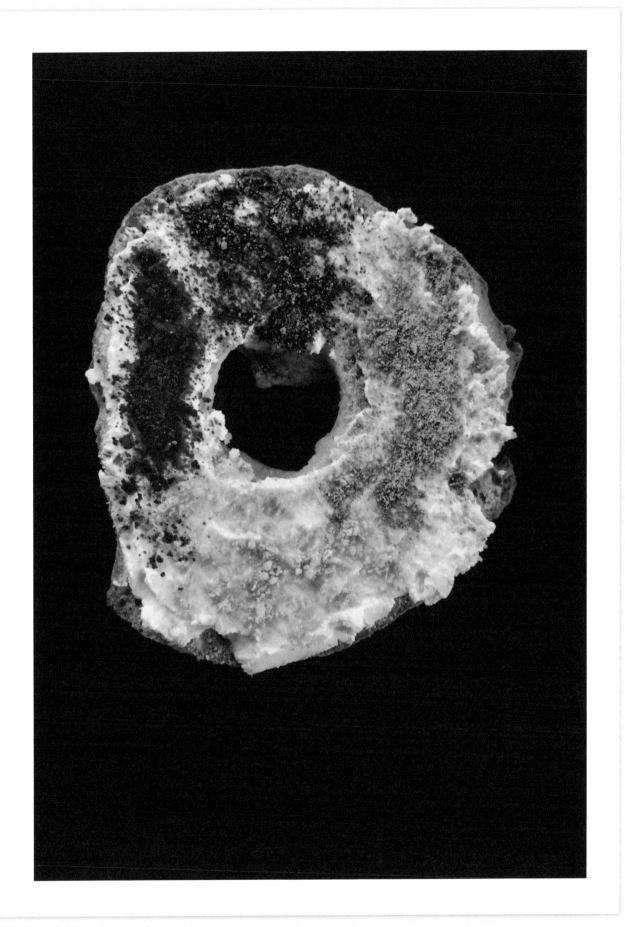

GREEN YELLOW RED:
A COLOURFUL EGG DANCE

Serves 4

Let's do a colourful egg dance together and immerse ourselves in a cosy feeling, of the slippery consistency of egg yolk. Green, Yellow, Red is the theme. It fulfils sensual desires and, believe me, it is more than just food; it is yummy. I love the epicurean and visual marriage between green spinach and yellow egg yolk (preferably runny). We will combine this with a red roasted root vegetable, namely beetroot (beet), which in winter is available in seasonal abundance.

We need to make a pasta dough first. For 4 people use 150 g plain (all-purpose) flour and 2 large eggs. Pile the flour into a mound on a work counter then make a well in the centre. Crack the eggs into the well and work the egg into the flour using a fork, in a circular motion. When the egg and flour are combined, add 1½ teaspoons of salt and 1 tablespoon of olive oil, kneading to form a silky dough. When the right consistency is achieved, cover and chill the dough for half an hour, in the refrigerator.

While the dough is chilling, prepare the filling from fresh spinach. I use a large amount of spinach leaves, about 1 kg, freshly washed and dripping wet, 6 cloves of garlic, sea salt, black pepper and 1 organic lemon. Now cut the garlic cloves into small slices and fry them with a nice drizzle of olive oil in a frying pan. After a short while, gradually add the wet spinach leaves, season with grated lemon zest, salt and pepper and finally squeeze in the wonderfully ripe tropical fruit and let the almost-sweet juice boil down a little, then turn off the heat and let the vegetables cool down.

In the meantime, prepare the colourful queen in red. A nice, firm, dark-red beetroot taproot is freed from its earthy skin using a peeler. The beetroot prepared in this way is shaved into slices as thin as possible using the peeler and the slices are placed on a baking sheet. Take a good-quality olive oil, drizzle it generously over the blood-red vegetable carpaccio and season with sea salt,

pepper and a sprig of rosemary, if one happens to be available. The oven should now be preheated to 220°C (430°F). Our aim is to make crispy beetroot chips.

Take the dough from the refrigerator and roll it out as thinly as possible. Cut out 8 dough circles with a diameter of about 10 cm (4 inches). Now it's time to make the ravioli: spread a tablespoon of the tasty spinach filling on 4 of the dough circles. Form a small hollow in the spinach using the back of a spoon and carefully place an egg yolk in each, then place another dough circle on top. Use a pastry brush to wet the edges of the dough with water and close, sealing the dough well. Prepare 1 large ravioli per person.

Meanwhile, put the baking sheet with the prepared beetroot into the preheated oven on the lowest shelf. The slices need about 20 minutes to crisp up. Before putting the ravioli into the water, the crisp red beetroot slices should be attractively arranged on large white plates.

Make a brown butter by melting 2 tablespoons butter in a pan over medium heat. Once it begins to froth, start whisking it until there are brown specks and it has a nutty aroma, then remove from the heat.

Bring salted water to the boil in a large saucepan, turn off the heat, drop in the ravioli and let them steep for just 2 minutes so that the egg yolk remains runny. Remove the cooked ravioli and carefully place them on top of the beetroot chips, sprinkle over fresh Parmesan and pour over the brown butter.

When eating, a wonderful colourfulness will spread out over the absolutely white plate like paint on a canvas and offer a visual event just as spectacular as the delicate treat for the palate.

Enjoy.

Essen, Sex und Kleider #1, 2021, Collage, 27.5 × 20 cm (10⅞ × 7⅞ inches).

Essen, Sex und Kleider #2, 2021, Collage, 27.5 × 20 cm (10⅞ × 7⅞ inches).

Essen, Sex und Kleider #3, 2021, Collage, 27.5 × 20 cm (10⅞ × 7⅞ inches).

HOW TO MAKE JAM
(AND SHARE WITH OTHERS)
BY DAVID ALLEN BURNS AND AUSTIN YOUNG / FALLEN FRUIT

THINGS YOU NEED:

PUBLIC FRUIT — LOCAL TREES THAT ARE
WELL WITHIN PUBLIC SPACE.
REUSABLE BAG FOR PICKED FRUIT
FRUIT PICKER
FRIENDS AND FAMILY
SIX — 8oz GLASS JAM JARS WITH LIDS
¼ CUP or 2 OUNCES or 1 PACKET OF PECTIN.
(OR LOW SUGAR PECTIN)
FIVE CUPS OF WHITE SUGAR
(SUGAR IS A NATURAL PRESERVATIVE)
12-14 PIECES OF FRUIT (THE SIZE OF AN ORANGE)
1 LARGE COOKING POT
1 LADLE OR A LARGE SPOON
1 CANNING FUNNEL
A YOUNG FRUIT TREE (TO PLANT IN SPRING)

THE BEST WAY TO MAKE JAM
IS WHEN YOU GO WITH FRIENDS
AND PICK THE FRUIT FROM PUBLIC SPACES.
THERE ARE FRUIT TREES THAT ARE IGNORED
ALONG STREETS, ALLEYS, AND PUBLIC PARKS
IN CITIES AROUND THE WORLD.
HARVEST THE FRUIT TREES
GO BY FOOT.   WHEN THE FRUIT IS RIPE.
TAKE A FRIEND,
SOMEONE FROM YOUR FAMILY
AND MAYBE A NEIGHBOR.
ONLY TAKE WHAT YOU NEED TO MAKE A BATCH OF JAM
(5-6 CUPS OF FRUIT, 12-14 ORANGES OR 16-20 PLUMS).
AS YOU WALK, MARK LOCATIONS OF
PUBLIC FRUIT TREES ON ENDLESSORCHARD.COM.
ALSO NOTE WHAT TIME OF YEAR THEY ARE RIPE.

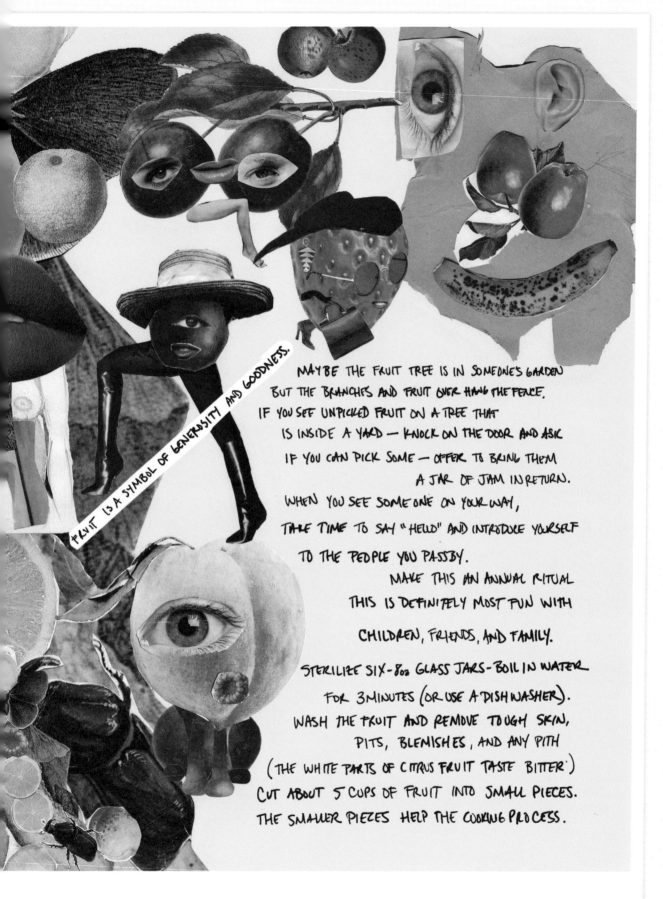

FRUIT IS A SYMBOL OF GENEROSITY AND GOODNESS.

MAYBE THE FRUIT TREE IS IN SOMEONE'S GARDEN
BUT THE BRANCHES AND FRUIT OVER HANG THE FENCE.
IF YOU SEE UNPICKED FRUIT ON A TREE THAT
    IS INSIDE A YARD — KNOCK ON THE DOOR AND ASK
    IF YOU CAN PICK SOME — OFFER TO BRING THEM
                    A JAR OF JAM IN RETURN.
WHEN YOU SEE SOMEONE ON YOUR WAY,
TAKE TIME TO SAY "HELLO" AND INTRODUCE YOURSELF
    TO THE PEOPLE YOU PASS BY.
                    MAKE THIS AN ANNUAL RITUAL
                    THIS IS DEFINITELY MOST FUN WITH
                    CHILDREN, FRIENDS, AND FAMILY.

STERILIZE SIX - 8oz GLASS JARS - BOIL IN WATER
    FOR 3 MINUTES (OR USE A DISH WASHER).
WASH THE FRUIT AND REMOVE TOUGH SKIN,
        PITS, BLEMISHES, AND ANY PITH
    (THE WHITE PARTS OF CITRUS FRUIT TASTE BITTER.)
CUT ABOUT 5 CUPS OF FRUIT INTO SMALL PIECES.
THE SMALLER PIECES HELP THE COOKING PROCESS.

PLACE CUT FRUIT AND PECTIN INTO A LARGE
COOKING POT ON THE STOVE AT MEDIUM HIGH HEAT.
STIR THE FRUIT CONTINUALLY TO
MAKE SURE THE HEAT IS EVENLY DISPERSED.
ADD A SMALL AMOUNT OF WATER OR LEMON JUICE
TO THE POT IF NEEDED TO MAKE
SURE THE FRUIT DOES NOT BURN.
WATCH THE JAM CAREFULLY AND
BRING TO A FULL BOIL.
AFTER A ROLLING BOIL, ADD THE SAME AMOUNT
OF SUGAR AS THE FRUIT (1:1 RATIO).
FOR LOW SUGAR PECTIN FOLLOW
THE DIRECTIONS ON PACKAGE.
KEEP STIRRING AND BRING IT TO A SECOND FULL BOIL.
IT TRANSFORMS QUICKLY FROM A YUMMY SAUCE
INTO DELICIOUS JAM.

ONE OF OUR FAVORITES
MEYER LEMON FIG LAVENDER JAM
DICE 4 CUPS OF FIGS
ZEST 4 LEMONS
REMOVE RINDS, PITH, SEEDS, AND MEMBRANES FROM 6-8 LEMONS
ADD FRUIT TO A LARGE POT, ADD PECTIN,
BRING TO A FULL BOIL, STIRRING CONTINUALLY.
ADD A SMALL AMOUNT OF LAVENDER TO THE JARS BEFORE FILLING THEM
ADD 4-5 CUPS OF SUGAR AND BRING TO SECOND BOIL

REMOVE FROM THE HEAT AND USE THE JAR FUNNEL
TO LADLE YOUR PUBLIC FRUIT JAM INTO THE 6 JARS.
QUICKLY, PUT THE LIDS ON TIGHT AND TURN
                    THE JARS UPSIDE DOWN.
THIS HELPS STERILIZE AND SEAL THE JARS.
    KEEP SOME FOR YOUR FAMILY
        AND SHARE THE REST WITH OTHERS.
    IN THE SPRING, PLANT A FRUIT TREE
            IN FRONT OF YOUR HOME
            NEXT TO THE SIDEWALK.

MAKE A SIGN THAT SAYS:

"THE FRUIT ON THIS TREE IS FOR SHARING
    WHEN IT'S RIPE, PICK ONLY WHAT YOU NEED
                        AND LEAVE THE REST."

    PLANT, MAP, AND SHARE YOUR FRUIT
            ENDLESSORCHARD.COM

IMAGE CREDIT: Selected images of fruit collages were created with the public for
FALLEN FRUIT MAGAZINE, V&A edition, Victoria and Albert Museum, London, 2019.

Southern-style Candied Yams

Serves 6 as a side dish

Ingredients

5 medium yams (or sweet potatoes)
8 tbsp salted butter
1 tsp ground cinnamon
¼ tsp ground cloves
½ tsp freshly grated nutmeg
¼ tsp ground ginger
1 cup brown sugar
¾ cup granulated sugar
1 tbsp pure vanilla extract
½ cup heavy cream (or double cream)

Method

Preheat the oven to 350°F (180°C).
Put the yams into a pot of water, bring to the boil over high heat. Boil the yams until the skins loosen and the yams are slightly softened but still firm. Allow to cool just enough to be able to handle them and then peel off the skin. (They should be easy to peel at this point, with the skin coming off with little effort.) Cut the yams into ½-inch (1-cm) slices and arrange in an 8 × 12-inch (20 × 30-cm) baking dish, layered in rows like fallen dominos.

For the candied mixture, melt the butter in a pan over low heat. Once melted, turn off the heat and add the cinnamon, cloves, nutmeg, ginger, ½ cup of the brown sugar, ½ cup of the granulated sugar, and the vanilla extract, then mix it all together. In a separate bowl, mix the remaining granulated sugar with the cream, then add this to the bowl with the butter and spices.

Pour the candied mixture over the yams, cover the dish with foil and cook for 25 minutes, then remove from the oven and baste the yams with the candied mixture. Sprinkle the top with the remaining brown sugar, then cover and return to the oven for another 20 minutes.

Allow the dish to sit for about 10 minutes before serving.

Images by Nicolas Polli
as featured in Wallpaper*
magazine's Artist's Palate
series, 2021.

BORN MEGHAN GORDON 1985; ARDEN SURDAM 1988 : LIVE LOS ANGELES, USA

To Foster a Fermented Honey Garlic –

—in memory of the dissipated body
a performance, installation, and spoonful of honey by Páll Haukur
facilitated by Studio Cooking
at the Armory Center for the Arts, Pasadena, California, US
on November 10, 2015

( ) Break skins to break apart the garlic bulbs.
Though the ye olde English gar means spear, garlics appear like swollen tears dotting your cutting board.

( ) With the cold flat of your knife push down upon each clove then strip its sheathing—
damaged cell walls release a sharp smell!
Both irritating and metaphoric, garlic yields compounds containing sulfur
aka the burning stone aka brimstone—
traditionally understood to be the smell of hell.
( ) Repeat.
( ) Place your newly crushed tears into a very clean jar.
( ) Stop when the glass is half-empty or full.[1]

( ) Gather honey from your mother or father land...
from the field of dandelions where you had your first kiss...
from within a lion killed in the land flowing with milk and honey...
or from your local farmers' market.

Differentiated by floral source, honeys are biologically tethered to roots and place and context:
if clover, if sage, if tupelo, if fireweed, if thyme, if acacia, if blue gum, if ironbark—then honey.

Are you into monofloral minimalism or are you an ethical polyfloralist?

Fun Fact To Help You Decide!
After a forager-bee collects its flower-nectar and regurgitates it into a hive-bee mouth, the almost-honey passes from one bee mouth to the next to the next for at least twenty minutes until deposited in honeycomb storage and sealed with wax

The only real rule here is: keep it raw [2]

( ) Slowly pour the honey into the jar
note clarity, viscosity, scent, translucence, speed, color, wettability, and taste
This ensures your future self has the means to appreciate the inevitable alchemical change
(before and after).
( ) Top the garlic with honey: submerge.
( ) Hermetically seal and walk away.

( ) Tomorrow: revolve the sealed jar to varnish the garlic.[3]
Your new circadian revolution is a jar flipped daily.
Until you notice bubbles[4]—a sign of life to be honored with
( ) a pre-flip twist of the lid.
Honey-garlic will exhale carbon dioxide, just like you!
When the bubbles cease[5]
when the garlic sinks
when the honey is runnier and all of it dark—
it's ready.

Though you may let it age for your own visual, sapid, or anticipatory pleasure,
fermented honey-garlic may be kept at room temperature for up to a year.[6]

---

1. The process will likely double the volume—a great investment!
2. Heated or treated honeys lose enzymes and yeast—both necessary for fermentation.
3. Mold may grow if the garlic is not covered with honey daily.
4. A few days' delay . . . but simply **( ) add a tablespoon or two of water to a bubble no-show.**
5. Perhaps a month after bubbling begins.
6. Three months in is an ideal time for a taste test.

<u>Chila</u> (homemade chickpea pancakes) is a very traditional dish in north-east India. It is often cooked in the morning for breakfast or sometimes in the evening as a snack. It is always eaten with coriander (cilantro) chutney.

Serves 4

Chila:

_ 200 g rice (any Indian rice)
_ 80 g *chana dal* (split chickpeas)
_ 2 handfuls coriander (cilantro)
_ 2 cloves garlic
_ ½ red onion
_ 1 tomato
_ 1 tablespoon olive oil, butter or ghee
_ salt, to taste

Coriander chutney:

_ 50 g coriander (cilantro)
_ 2 cloves garlic
_ 2 tablespoons olive oil or mustard oil
_ juice of 1 lemon
_ 2 green chillies
_ 1 tablespoon water
_ 1 tablespoon salt

Put the rice and *chana dal* (split chickpeas) into a pot or bowl, cover with water and leave to soak overnight.

The next day, drain the rice and *chana dal* and transfer to a blender, adding a little fresh water (to help it blend properly). Blend it until it's neither too thick nor too runny, then add salt to taste. Transfer to a bowl.

Blend a handful of coriander (cilantro) and the garlic separately then add them to the bowl with the rice and *chana dal* liquid, and mix well to make a batter.

Chop the onion, tomato and a handful of coriander and add to the batter.

Heat a frying pan (skillet) over medium heat. Add 1 tablespoon of olive oil, butter or ghee (your choice). When the pan is hot, add 4 tablespoons of the batter and let it cook, turning once, until slightly browned on both sides. Serve straight away, while hot. Repeat the process using the remaining batter.

For the coriander chutney, blend all the ingredients together in a blender. Voilà.

Serve the *chila* hot from the pan with the chutney, and season to taste.

Jungli Maas

_ 6 tablespoons ghee
_ 1½ large red onions, coarsely chopped
_ 2 teaspoons coriander seeds, ground
  in a mortar with a pestle
_ 10–12 cloves garlic, lightly crushed
_ 1 kg mutton (it can be with or without
  the bone, both work, and any part of
  lamb or goat that you like), cut
  into chunks
_ 4 potatoes, peeled and halved
_ salt, to taste
_ Indian bread or rice, to serve

For making your own
garam masala powder:

_ 1 star anise (optional)
_ 1 blade mace (optional)
_ 10 cloves
_ 1 tablespoon black pepper
_ 1½ teaspoons cumin seeds
_ 7 dried red chillies
_ 5-cm (2-inch) cinnamon stick
_ 4 black cardamom pods
_ 1 teaspoon ground turmeric
_ 4 bay leaves

Start by making the garam masala. Put all the garam masala ingredients into a spice grinder and grind to a powder. Store in a jar until needed.

For the curry, heat the ghee in a heavy pan (use one with a lid) over medium heat. Add the onions and fry, stirring, until they're golden brown and soft. Make sure you stir the onions constantly so they don't burn. Add the coriander seeds and garlic and fry for 1 minute further. Add the mutton, the garam masala, season with salt and cook over high heat for 5 minutes, stirring.

Now pour in 125 ml water, cover the pan with the lid and let it simmer over a low heat for 10–15 minutes. Stir every 4 minutes. Add the potatoes and 250 ml water to the pan and cook over a very, very low heat for another hour. Every 10 minutes, take the lid off and stir well.

Serve hot with any Indian bread or rice.

THE ARAB BARBER

(After a most devilish adventure, fleeing
the accursed fumes and fulminating rays and
sparks of the infernal furnaces and the claws
of Mephistopheles, our plucky champion of the
magical arts, Dr. Faustus, is found wandering
in the solitude of arid parts.)

Who'd have guessed, but deep in the desolate dunes
lay a tortuous path out of the Devil's nest. A tunnel
hidden in the sand, full of fiendish flames and foul
sulphurous odours, from whence passers-by could
hear the fear of the damned and the lashes of
demons whipping the supplicant hordes.

Having escaped through this tunnel, Faustus
walked on alone as if in a waking dream, trudging
night and day through an unimaginable scene:
yellow sand all around and dunes and scorching
heat and an occasional cactus. And there he
roamed in the rolling sand, clad in but a piece of
plaid, a wretched soul, suffused with suppurating
sores. For in that infernal underworld from which
he had fled, he had been fiendishly tortured with
a mouldy needle, scarring his face and marring his
body with pustules and pestilent pimples. He was,
you might say, in quite awful shape.

Whereupon, faint and weak, amid the desert dunes
and trepidations, through the pink haze of the
dawn's sensations a marshland reared into view of
fresh green grass and palm trees all around, with
dates and budgies and – surprise! – a camel lying
upon the ground. It was the famous ship of the
desert with its two lardy lumps that Faustus had
seen in books on the nomadic Saracens. Tall and
majestic like in an illustration, this was a mount
worthy of such a location. The beast was dressed
in the Arabian manner, with a leather saddle on
a colourful rug, a heavy holster, a scimitar of war
and a goatskin of water, not to mention grandly
garnished garments on its humps that suggested
it belonged to some moneyed Moorish majesty.

Drawing cautiously close to such plentiful miracles,
in the water could be seen the sprawling owner of
this exotic steed: a portly vizier soaping himself in
the oasis. And, good lord, with such vigour! With
a long, bristle brush he scrubbed the recesses of
his rather rotund figure. These habits were clearly
a routine affair that filled the sweet-scented air
and, at the edge of the bog, beside the spring,
stood soaps and shampoos and essences and oils,
plus a set of gilded golden towels, arranged as
a beach bather might in the Algarve, along with
other scattered sorts of special spices. For an

in-looking onlooker, it was a most serious scene, even a joy to behold for its salubriousness and hygiene.

As he whistled in his bath, the Caliph was completely oblivious to the person approaching his camel. Furtively, Faustus grabbed hold of the cord that precariously secured the creature in place. Without a word of warning, he jumped astride the beast, astonishing it with jabs, admonishing it – 'Giddy-up! Let's go camel!' – to get up and flee, and as fast as possible. Predictably, said desert mount took fright and in a thrice tossed off the knight, who flew backwards into the caliph's bath, there in the Arabian quagmire.

So thick and white were the suds that cleansed his grace that the magician's roar produced a fog that inundated this other part of the desert. It was – how to explain? – a dense and balsamic cloud that with this other water from the spring, cleaned hair, beard and skin, leaving not the faintest sign of dirt and grime. A bleach, indeed. And boy was that foam frothy! In vain the vizier and the wizard fought for air amid the scum. The haste with which the camel had struck Faustus on the nose had created a castle of vapours of lavender and geranium and rose. And amid this vexing scene both

a hopeless vizier and Faustus were fighting for air as if in a battle – a galling state for both but especially the sprawling cream of Moorish finance – this most noble naked Arab was, as one might say in the Queen's English, up shit's creek without a paddle.

For an on-looking incomer wondering if this was a mirage, it would surely have seemed that a sheet of sheep's wool had arisen in this other part of Arabia. It was a phenomenon worthy of one thousand and one nights and of seventy-two heavenly virgins washing their hair.

Supremely supportive of another man's suffering and his own maladies, Faustus recalled a simple spell that produced wind with just a pouting puff and a mere rhythmic click of the fingers.

Click click, blow; click click, blow blow! A magical gust like a glassy ghoul flew across the flat oasis. For an on-looking incomer, they would have seen, as if in a waking dream, a castle of spume rise up a dune, slide slowly over the sand and pause on a peak within reach of the beach.

Faustus and the vizier, whom it was found had the unusual name of Aladdin Al-Maduzhal, then had the chance to acquaint themselves one with the other.

On asking if t'other was of Christian faith, Faustus could see that was not the case, for he thanked him for the magic with a foreign salaam. Later with silver he crossed his palm and offered friendship and gifts, since Aladdin believed in fate, and what he had seen was an unusual intervention and purpose that would later conflate.

While the gentlemen were engrossed in ceremonial matters, in the syrupy pond that came up to their waist, a most visible difference was seen in the face. For while Faustus exhibited the marks of torment and torture and agony, the vizier overflowed with good health and plenty. Interestingly, both he and the camel gnawed a kind of caramel. It was a stress-reducing bubble gum. And in the fountains the vizier wore something peculiar attached to his ears and the bridge of his nose with two dark glass beads in front of his eyes. An odd thing that he later explained was a pair of shaded oscula, a remedy for cataracts, that well-known ocular ailment. Both inventions, for which he was lauded, had caught on among the silk caravanners roaming the East and Iran and India and Pakistan.

Needless to say that a mutual esteem transpired and was cemented. And on the beach Aladdin presented Faustus with a private pair of his own shades, a rare object so light it could barely be felt upon the face, and whose turtle shell frame was grooved and polychromatic and the darkened lenticular beads of a strength to read letters that were tiny, normal and emphatic. An osculum for all purposes, to see up close and from far away, especially under the glaring glow of the Al-Saudi sun.

Incidentally, the vizier Al-Maduzhal was a veritable vade mecum of the vernacular variety, a notable author of fabulous formulas of pomades and poultices, lotions and essential oils, tantric therapies and medicinal remedies. His mastery was extolled for ailments as diverse as: abscesses and aphthae in the digestive and restive tract, inflammations and affections of the oesophagus and aerophagus, asthma and anaemia of the pulmonic sacs, to the left, right and out of sight, bruising and diurnal and nocturnal frights, burns, caries of the teeth and bone and the soft cartilage where aches are prone, chilblains, chills, cleft lip, thick or thin, colics and congestions from inspiring, expiring and respiring, conjunctivitis and oedemas of the sight and the skin around the eyes, lashes, lids and brows, cysts, dermatitis of every shape and sort and of all inclined and intractable parts of the complexion, erectile and retractile dysfunction, dry and phlegmy coughs, fevers of the yellow kind and other colours, including blue, which as one knows is not topical in origin but

revolting in the encephalon, gastritis, goitre and gonorrhoea, herpes and haemorrhoids, infections of every shape and sort, incontinence, in-growing toenails, insect bites and stings, kidney stones and other internal blockages, lupus vulgaris, madness, measles, migraines, mumps and myopia, narcissism and nausea, obesity, obstipation and otitis of the tympana, timpani and tympanites, pimples and pneumonia, rage, rheumatism and rickets, scabies, sclerosis, scurvy, shingles and sores, tetanus, teeth-gnashing and TB, ulcers, varicose veins and virilism, and warts; in other words, he had a cure and a diagnosis for all sorts: just chew a caramel and change your lunettes. Apparently, Aladdin had an endless collection and a particular predilection for this type of apparel. With his countless pairs of oscula he osculated a diverse range of disparate diseases of the body and mind. He was a most prodigal and prodigious physician.

Faustus, in turn, shared a series of mysteries of the soul and of alchemy and of wizardry, such as: divining from the entrails of billy goats and baby goats and other reared beasts, divining from the flight of birds and dew drops and rainwater in pots and in tea mugs and coffee cups, and when molten wax falls into water or when looking into the fire or at the shape of the clouds, and divining by means of auguries, as for example, when you hear the croak of a frog, and divining with the small bones of the distal, middle and proximal phalanx, or with the wrist bones of martyrs, and when these pieces or whelks are thrown in the air and leave marks that are magical letters, and how to interpret the stars from the constellations and create horoscopes, and also how to read the celestial bodies nearby like the Moon that control the human humours and the monsoons, and also the water that flows freely under the earth that one finds with a magnetic pendulum or two rods platinized with gold, and, also, from the special forebodings of the meteors and eclipses, and the catastrophes they presage, and of when the sun disappears, and night becomes day with no warning, and what it means, and of many other prophecies, for example, when scary things appear in the dreams that lead to nightmares, and of when in a dream one finds an empty box or a tooth falls out, and of the amulet for the evil eye and bad omens and bewitching, and other black arts of horrific plight, and of how talismans and charms and rabbit feet work around one's neck or deep in one's pocket, and of horseshoes fixed on frontispieces, and of garlic and salt against spirits and the vampyric souls of the damned that wish us ill and drink our blood, and of what one seeks, for one and all, in the crystal ball, and of how the damned talk through electric appliances, and of the photo images that appear

in soups, and on suits when ruined with dirt stains and wine spots, and of the fathomless sense of the syllable when it whispers enigmas in the ear, and of reading one's fate in the tarot cards and one's future in the palm of the hand, and of the other arts of the Egyptians and Etruscans and gipsies, and on beings from other dimensions and planets, winged beings, and of angels and archangels, and demons and little imps, and of the devil and his ill-mannered and cursed helpers, and of heaven and hell and purgatory, and of how to talk to the dead and corpses, and to know if they wish us ill, or are nice deceased people from this part of the universe or another.

For an incoming out-looker observing said conference, he would have witnessed a great seminar on life and time and the world. Faustus had just begun to speak of magic when the other said: 'Doctor, please excuse the interruption, but I notice you have a serious skin eruption'. And, indeed, a bowed Faustus avowed, so he did. He could not rest or sleep such was the itch he felt in his feet and other parts of his body. Scabies maybe? Aladdin looked closer and proclaimed, 'They are pustules!' Pressing lightly and slightly a piggybacking testicle on the magician's shoulder revealed that a suppurating serum was concealed in the pimples. Recounting his prior adventure, Faustus told of the pus-filled fiend who had poked him with a venomous spike full of spittle. It must have been poisonous, said the physician. With his index finger, prodding the pustules here and there, blood poured from the intumescent boils that were bigger. Now you see them, now you don't. Then, for the smaller ones, he placed leeches on the sorcerer's skin that he fetched from the bottom of the pool. Referring to the medieval method of letting blood, he said, 'The best remedies are old school!'

Finally, he mentioned, 'I am familiar with a fabulous active principle, a blessing for blisters and a whole host of infectious inflammations. A topical tonic that soothes itching and swelling and gives a lift to the face – giving both skin and body hair a radiant grace!' 'And what syrup is this?' asked Faustus. 'It's a cactus!' In fact, at the edge of the water, the vizier pointed to an enormous fleshy leaf with spiky thorns. And the physician immediately set about preparing the following recipe for aloe vera cream.

With a spatula remove the jelly formed by the fleshy pulp of the cactus. Place in a receptacle. Be careful with the thorns. Then, in a heated pan, make a sugary syrup with sweet water. Remove before it hardens. Wait to cool and add the cactus gel and a natural thickener (like the one made from quince peel) and plenty of lemon oil. Stir at a low heat, do not boil, until it forms a spreadable salve. Keep in a dry place. Spread on wounds, use to wash hair and to moisturize your ear. It is also good to eat!

After preparing the poultice into a kind of mayonnaise, Aladdin spread the balm on his skin as if to show Faustus how to begin. Standing there with ointment on his abdomen, the Moor had the appearance of an admirable snowman. Then, licking the remedy from his digits, he opined that the custard-coloured compound was one of a kind, for it was unusually nourishing despite the tang. Faustus confirmed it had a certain twang, to which he added that if chilled the mélange would make a passable blancmange. 'And what's more, it lasts for months in the cold store!' said the physician, who, still covered in the cream, fetched his sharp sword from the saddle of the camel and began shaving his legs, and then his jaw and his maw and his paw. Raving that he preferred this paste to any other to depilate and epilate the nether regions of his being, he finished the job. A cleaner barber there was not.

Faustus applied the pomade according to the advice and thanked him for the gesture.
    End of the adventure.

Epilogue
In a Turkish tent erected a slight distance from the baths in the Al-Saudi desert, where we leave the two hermits preening their skin and complexion with utmost attention, they were now joined by the vizier's suite of servants, with Arabic odalisques and eunuchs amok and weaponized warriors, ready to make that wilderness a ministry of mystery – a university where these two prestigious personages would immerse themselves in fabulous discoveries of the logical and the irrational, of the proportional and the unmeasurable, of the old and the new.

And as our lordships discussed pedagogy, and whether it was science or something other than thaumaturgy, Aladdin recalled that Faustus could talk to cadavers. (To be continued...)

A caramel for a camel: the recipe for Aladdin
Al-Maduzhal's chewy pastille

Of all the vizier Al-Maduzhal's most celebrated
concoctions, there was one, a top seller in every
bazaar and emporium across Arabia, that was
also devoutly prized by all those with little time
to devote to oral hygiene. It was but a mere
caramel but from its appearance and purpose
a most unique pastille.

Designed purely for mastication, this pseudo-
victual awarded the palate and protected the
dentition. It could be chewed until one became
weary or bored and so was collected by many
an individual, above all those whose office obliged
long journeys carrying valuable goods on the
caravans and trade routes of the Orient.

Along Silk Street, as the main route was called,
it was common for caravanners to stock up on
this gum for the duration of the trip. Each might
possess just a single caramel or a variety in a
range of flavours, which they would gnaw at their
pleasure as they plodded through the desert. In
these circumstances, when a nomad was sated
from munching this morsel, he could stow it away
and pop it back in his mouth whenever he wished,
only requiring a new one if it fell on the floor; or if
the flavour of a particular caramel fatigued him
and he preferred another aroma; or if by mistake
the gum was ingested.

In this case, it was perfectly harmless if digested,
being entirely excreted in the stool at a later
date, often aiding a person to evacuate. 'Doctor
Al-Maduzhal's sweet relief!' was how the more
sedentary of caravanners described this treat,
resorting to this solution of soothing relaxation for
that bothersome malady – traveller's constipation.

But the virtues of this panacea were far wider
in scope. All those who, like a camel, suffered
unfortunate infections of the mouth and morbid
halitosis, could now seek succour from this very
expedient to suppress any bad odour exhaled by
the breath, and engage in chitchat without fear
of disturbing their audience.

The caramel kiss was also all the rage in Arabia.

However, Aladdin could not lay sole claim to the
astonishing inventing of the perpetual pastille.
Much of the credit for this epic episode was owed
to a patient who visited the vizier following a turn
of heartburn, soothing his discomfort by chewing
a chunk of dry meat between meals. Inspired
by this poor man, Aladdin designed a substance
that, when placed in the mouth, required no
consumption, but simulated the action of
consuming. Aladdin himself lost ten pounds from

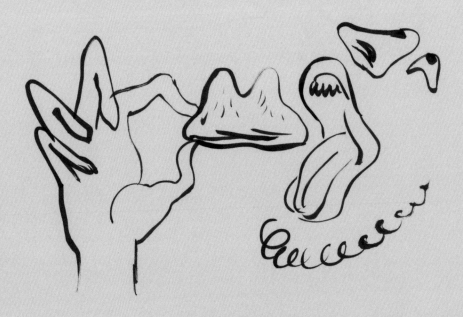

apparently consuming a gum when nothing in fact had been consumed. The caramel tones the jaw and the navel – it keeps you lean and your teeth clean!

The perpetual pastille permitted a very versatile and discrete use from person to person, adapting to the ailment of each and every one.

However, a few people began to adulterate the original recipe for the caramel by adding resins and molasses so they could create inflatable breakable balls and baskets. This habit saddened Aladdin greatly, who referred to the perpetual pastille as his legacy, detesting the sight of someone fiddling with what he considered a good and serious remedy. Those persons and personages who unduly adulterated the caramel to fill spheres were thugs.

Here, finally, is Aladdin's original recipe to produce his prestigious perpetual pastille, free of conservatives and preservatives, of alcohol and alkaloids, and of resins and resinates:

In a big pot full of water, place another pot a little smaller, but still large, to steam this latter pan, and make a bain-marie. Warm within this a quarter (give or take 14 kg) of beeswax until melting, stir, adding a ⅕ of a quarter of Arabic syrup – basically a broth boiled with sugars and aromas (1.5 parts sugar, 1 part water, ¹⁄₁₀ part bitter lemon and ¹⁄₁₀ part tea of orange flower). After boiling for

10 minutes, it is ready to mix with the molten beeswax and another half-quarter of finely powdered sugarcane.

Now add a little flavour to this dough-like excipient. While constantly stirring the molten mixture in the pot, add one of these three essences:

1.   three sticks of cinnamon
2.   two tablespoons of strawberry jam
3.   a generous heap of flowering cloves

And stir and stir, letting the aroma merge with the waxy caramel dough until they each take on the taste of the other. Then, losing no time, pour the amalgamated mixture onto a baking tray previously sprinkled with powdered sugar, and let it set hard and cold. With a large knife, cut the rigid dough into separate squares the size of a nut. Use the same sugar powder to separate the pieces, and swirl the sweeties in a pan so they are covered in this copious and candied powder. Arrange the cold squares and, one by one, wrap them in wrappers of sesame oil paper emblazoned with iconoclastic and eclectic motifs.

It's wholesome and it's tasty, but one buys with one's eyes: so says the vizier Al-Maduzhal.

And voilà!
End of the recipe.

CHEESE

Ingredients

48 oz cream cheese
12 oz goat cheese
½ lemon squeezed
Salt it up
1 jalapeño
1 bunch cilantro
handful chopped chive
lots of veggies!

Something round like:
small pumpkin
small watermelon
big ball of cream cheese

Dedicated to Joella Johnson, my Grandma.
Untitled [Face #1 Joella Johnson] 1998. 24 x 20 inches (61 x 51 cm).

LYLE'S GREENS
Serves 2–4

extra virgin olive oil
1 red onion, chopped
leek, washed and chopped thinly
3–4 cloves garlic, chopped
7–9 shiitake mushrooms, stems removed
  and sliced thinly
vegan chipotle sausages or any vegan sausage
  of your choice
2 bunches of hearty greens, such as collard
  greens and Lacinato kale (cavolo nero)
  or collard greens with beet (beetroot)
  or dandelion greens
2–3 tablespoons low-sodium tamari or
  liquid aminos seasoning, to taste
1 teaspoon garlic powder
crushed red pepper (chilli flakes), to taste

In a large pan, heat the olive oil over a medium heat and add the onion, leek, and garlic. Sauté for about 5 minutes until translucent.

Stir in the shiitake mushrooms and cook until soft, about another 5 minutes.

Quarter the chipotle sausages lengthwise and slice thinly. Stir them into the onion, leek, and mushroom mixture once the mushrooms are soft, and sauté for another 5 minutes.

Using a slotted spoon, remove the onion, leek, mushroom, and sausage mixture from the pan, transfer to a plate and keep warm.

Thinly chop the two kinds of greens of your choice.

Sometimes I stem the greens and sometimes I don't—it depends on my mood. Stems are good for roughage … so most times I keep them … but if I'm cooking for holidays or a party, I often cut them out.

Add a splash more olive oil to the pan (keep whatever is left in the pan to add flavor) and raise the temperature to medium-high, then add the greens. Sauté the greens for 3 minutes. Stir in the onion, leek, mushroom, and sausage mixture and toss to combine.

Add the tamari or liquid aminos, garlic powder, and crushed red pepper (chilli flakes) and mix well.

Let it simmer on a low heat for 5–7 minutes, stirring occasionally. The greens should still be slightly crunchy and vibrantly green.

Note 1: Serve with salmon, Japanese yams (not as sweet as American yams), and pepper sauce for a real treat.
Note 2: Use any leftover greens in a frittata.

Opposite, clockwise from top left: Trying to stay sane in New Garden in Germantown, NY. Dedicated to George Floyd, May 27, 2020; First harvest, jalapeño pepper; Shiitake mushrooms; and Sautéd greens. Below, clockwise from top left: Collard greens with white navy beans; Good morning frittata with leftover greens; and Mixed greens, heirloom, and plum.

INGREDIENTS
Makes 20 faces

120 g egg whites (from 2–3 large eggs)
a few drops of lemon juice
150 g caster (superfine) sugar
pinch of salt
pinch of cornstarch (cornflour)
pinch of baking powder
natural food dyes like annatto, matcha
   (green tea), turmeric, beetroot (beet)
   powder or elderberry juice (please use
   organic products!)

METHOD

Preheat the oven to 120°C (250°F).

Place the egg whites and lemon juice in a clean, dry mixing bowl. Whisk using a hand whisk or an electric mixer until foamy. Slowly add the sugar, salt, cornstarch (cornflour) and baking powder, and continue to whisk the mixture until it becomes thick and glossy. Colour the meringue mixture using your chosen natural food dyes.

Fill a pastry (piping) bag with the dyed meringue mixture, snip off the end and draw 20 faces (10–15 cm/4–6 inches wide) on a baking sheet lined with baking paper. You may need more than one pastry bag if you have dyed the meringue different colours.

Place the meringue faces in the preheated oven on the middle shelf and bake for 1 hour. Turn off the oven. Open the oven door and leave the meringues on the baking sheet until cool.

Enjoy!

Pasta with Red Pesto
Serves 4

-

100 g pine nuts
500 g spaghetti
olive oil
1 potato
280 g sun-dried tomatoes in oil, drained
3–5 dried chillies
2–3 cloves garlic
100 g Parmesan, grated
100 g triple-concentrated tomato paste
and some basil for decoration
salt

-

Toast the pine nuts in a frying pan over low heat.

Cook the spaghetti in a large pan of boiling salted
water with a dash of olive oil, preferably with
a potato – not for too long, just until al dente, then
drain (reserve 250 ml of the cooking water) and
return the spaghetti to the pan.

Now put the toasted pine nuts into a blender with
the sun-dried tomatoes, dried chillies, garlic cloves,
grated Parmesan and tomato paste.

Blend everything, stir in the reserved pasta water
and then add the pesto sauce to the pasta and mix.
Serve on plates and garnish with basil.

The Brutalist Kitchen Manifesto

1.   Brutalist Kitchen is a dogma kitchen where certain
     rules apply.
2.   The main rule is the following: ingredients are used
     alone for a certain dish; only water and salt may be added.
2a. An example: instead of Duck with Orange Sauce, Duck
     with Duck Sauce is prepared. Salads are more difficult,
     as oils or juices from other plants are forbidden.
3.   Different (prepared) ingredients are not permitted on the
     same plate. They have to be presented as different units.
     The different foods may be served at the same time.
3a. The eater may thus combine the tastes of different
     ingredients while eating.
3b. Instead of a chef imposing what should go together
     and in which amount for a given serving, the eater makes
     these decisions.
4.   There is an exception: liquids like soups and stocks
     do generally require the combination of ingredients,
     but they should be treated like the nutrients that the
     plant, mushroom or animal has taken up before being
     used in Brutalist Kitchen.
4a. The taste of a certain ingredient is, in itself, partly
     the result of different food sources for this ingredient.
5.   The use of overlooked, hard-to-get or rare ingredients,
     or ingredients that are generally discarded, is characteristic
     of Brutalist Kitchen.
5a. Generally speaking, Brutalist Kitchen is less about
     recipes and more about finding and preparing ingredients.
5b. One ingredient is often divided and cooked in different
     ways and then added again on the same plate. For instance,
     a large mushroom is divided into pieces, which are grilled,
     steamed, cooked etc.; a sauce is made from the lamellae

at low heat overnight; then all is placed together again before serving.

6.   Elaborate cooking techniques are allowed, as is raw or quickly heated food.

6a. Brutalist Cuisine is not about a lack of sophistication, but a lack of combination of different ingredients and a commitment to purity.

7.   Decoration on the plate is avoided.

8.   Portions tend to be of substantial size.

9.   Brutalist Cooking has its origins in traditional Mediterranean or Japanese cuisine, but is neither Mediterranean nor Japanese.

10. To our knowledge, there is as yet not one restaurant in the world today that deserves to be called essentially Brutalist, with a kitchen committed to these guidelines.

10a. People sometimes cook Brutalist at home.

11. We are born as Brutalist eaters, as mother's milk is essentially Brutalist.

12. Brutalist Kitchen is named in reference to Brutalist architecture, renowned for its linear and blockish appearance.

13. In Orthodox (or Ultra-Orthodox) Brutalist Cuisine, neither water nor salt is added. Water may be extracted from the ingredient, e.g. by distillation or centrifugation.

Previous spread, top to bottom: Broccoli Parthenon, Restauranglabbet, Stockholm, 2019; Apple Fanny, Restauranglabbet, Stockholm, 2019; Opposite, top to bottom: Mushroom Carsten, Trois Mec, Los Angeles, 2019; Yellow Pea Vreta, Trois Mec, Los Angeles, 2019. All dishes prepared by chefs Stefan Eriksson and Johan Gottberg.

This recipe was introduced to me at Ristorante Trattoria Manueli, on the outskirts of Faenza, west of Ravenna in Italy, where the owners were quick to defer the recipe origins to the region itself.

Although persimmons can be frozen and thawed to force ripening, they lose a bit of their joy. That method is fine for use in breads or margaritas, but fresh, ripe persimmons are needed here.

Ripe hachiya persimmons are a deep orangey-red. Their jelly-like interior seems to be on the verge of breaking through the nearly translucent skin. I try to wait until I notice the skin begin to sag.

When the crown of the fruit gives way to the touch, it is ready.

The perfect persimmon is important because the unripe ones have a very disturbing astringency. My first experience eating one felt like having a mouthful of black rabbit hair, an experience I would maybe save only for enemies.

Persimmon Parfait

Serves 4

4–5   ripe hachiya persimmons, see note above
½   cup heavy (double) cream, whipped softly
2   candied chestnuts or praline pecans or 6 tablespoons chestnut cream spread

To prepare the persimmons:
Hold a ripe persimmon in your palm, stem facing up. Grab hold of the leaf close to the center and very slowly pull it off the fruit. Using a spoon, gently scoop into the fruit between the skin and the flesh. Run it along the inside of the thin skin to release the section of flesh into a bowl. Very gently scrape out the remaining pulp from the skin and mash it with the back of your spoon in the bowl. Repeat with the remaining fruit. For those who are challenged by food textures like oysters, simply press the flesh through a sieve using the back of the spoon to make a smooth thick glaze and then proceed.

To assemble the parfait:
Use a tall glass for a layered parfait; it invokes childhood and asks for a long spoon.

Finish with a bit of nut:
Alternate layers of mashed persimmon and whipped cream, finishing at the rim with the cream. Sprinkle or swirl your choice of nut—the Manueli version is topped with crumbled candied chestnut pieces, and I love the crunch. A few crushed praline pecans work as well. My standby version substitutes them with the chestnut cream spread as we generally have a tube in our pantry. Serve at room temperature or slightly chilled.

THE WATER CYCLE

— glass filled with seawater
  from the closest ocean
— tequila

Fill glass with water from the
closest ocean and place on a sunny
windowsill. Let the water evaporate
completely. Leave the salt in the
glass. Pour in tequila and drink.

THE WANDERING IN FOGGY MORNING MUSHROOM SOUP

— foggy morning
— wandering in a forest
— mushrooms
— onion
— butter
— stock
— parsley
— sherry
— spices + herbs
— hazelnuts

On a foggy morning in the autumn,
wander through a forest and gather
edible mushrooms. Sweat the
mushrooms and the onion in a pot
with butter. Add stock and parsley and
simmer. Blend if desired. Add sherry.
Spice to taste. Top off with chopped
fresh herbs and crushed roasted
hazelnuts. As you eat remember the
main ingredients are the wandering
in a forest and the foggy morning.

THE JOHN CAGE OMELETTE

— eggs
— spices and/or fresh herbs
— butter or oil

Beat desired amount of eggs in a bowl. Randomly pick three or four spices or herbs from your kitchen with your eyes closed. Add to eggs and cook with butter or oil.

Come again to the

where everything you like

Cookery, conversati

are waiting, sometimes e

ttle Kitchen

ll likes you.

THE LITTLE MIRROR IN
TCHEN REFLECTED THE
Y OF YOU, FROM THE END
A WHITE JACKET TO THE
F YOUR GLEAMING PRICK,
PPED COOKING IN RESPONSE
UR INNOCENT INVITATION TO
AT YOU WERE SEEING AND
Y EYES BE DAZZLED AND
UL BE CHARMED.

+ concupiscence

n impatiently, for you.

Spaghetti with Lobster

2 live lobsters
1½ pounds each
1/3 cup olive oil
1 clove garlic, minced
1 small onion, chopped
1 teaspoon salt
1/4-1/2 tsp. cayenne pepper
Fresh black pepper
1 cup canned tomatoes
2 tablespoons tomatoe paste
2 tablespoons water
2/3 cup dry white wine
1½ tablespoons chopped parsley
1 teaspoon oregano
1 pound pasta

① Wash lobsters. Cut spinal cord by inserting knife where tail + body meet. Turn lobsters on their backs + split lengthwise. Cut each tail in 3 peices. Cut off claws + crack.

② Heat oil in skillet. Add lobsters. Cook over high heat 3 or 4 minutes till red. Add garlic, onion, seasonings and cook, stirring, 5 minutes.

③ Add tomatoes + tomatoe pasta blended with water + cook turning constantly one minute.

④ Add wine, parsley, and oregano + cook about ten minutes turning frequently.

⑤ Pour sauce over spaghetti + garnish platter with lobster.

cacio e pepe

ingredients:

    pecorino romano

    black peppercorns

    tonnarelli (can substitute with rigatoni or spaghetti)

You need only these 3 ingredients. No more. No less.

instructions:

1. grate the pecorino romano. (the finer the better)
2. crush the black peppercorns
3. bring water to boil
   season with salt
   add the pasta
4. while pasta is boiling, hold bowl with cheese and pepper over the boiling pot to warm the bowl.
5. mix the warmed cheese and pepper and add a little pasta water to make it creamy.
6. when the pasta is ready, scoop it directly from the pot into the bowl of cheese and pepper and mix.
7. If sauce is too watery grate more cheese. If it is not creamy enough add pasta water.
8. serve with some grated cheese and pepper on top.

note: For measurements you will learn through the process. I do not measure the ingredients, I know from my senses.

Emily Jacir
ROMA
2020

BORN JOHANNA JACKSON 1968; CHRIS JOHANSON 1972 : LIVE PORTLAND, OREGON, USA

RELLENOS CASSEROLE
////////////////////////////////
Serves 4—6

12—14 (about 22 ounces) Poblano or Anaheim peppers (In the summer
up here in Portland, Oregon, we picked a bunch of peppers at a farm.
They had some amazing Romanian peppers that I used additionally.)

20 oz tomato sauce (passata)

½ onion, roughly chopped

2—3 cloves garlic

grapeseed oil (or other vegetable oil), for frying

1 bay leaf

1—3 teaspoons crushed red pepper (chilli flakes), to taste

pinch of cayenne pepper (optional)

2—3 eggs

2 oz all-purpose (plain) flour (or use gluten-free oat flour
or potato flour, or a mixture)

½ cup of some kind of milk

12 oz round, hard Mexican <u>queso</u> (one that comes in a package
with water in it), crumbled; use about three quarters of the round.
Any cheese can work, although maybe not blue cheese, but I have had
success with cashew cheese when I made straight up <u>chiles</u> <u>rellenos</u>.

salt and pepper

salad, to serve

I like to free-form cook, so this recipe is loosey-goosey. Up here
in Portland, Oregon, at the time of year when it's getting cold
and rainy, I can really start to miss California. And with the
pandemic weirdness I've found I'm thinking a lot about my decades
in California growing up. This dish conjures up the 1970s food
I grew up with by way of casseroles and my favorite food to this
day, which is all the wonderful varieties of Mexican food I eat
when cruising around down there.

First thing you do is prepare the peppers by broiling (grilling)
them in the oven until the skin is burned and blistered. Take them
out of the oven and place them in a plastic bag or a in bowl with a
lid and cover the bowl with a dish towel. Leave it for 20 minutes or
so, allowing time for the moisture to hang out in there and further
loosen the skins from the peppers. Take the peppers out one at a
time and take off the stems and remove and discard the seeds. I do
this with a spoon. Open them up and flatten them, then set aside.

Then get out a blender and put in the tomato sauce. If it was still
summer, I'd pick some tomatoes from my yard, boil the skins off,
core them and add them too. Add the onion and the garlic to the
blender. Blend it up.

Then, in a non-reactive pan that has a lid, heat some oil. I'm using grapeseed oil, but you could use olive oil, avocado oil, or whatever you have. Maybe I'd say don't use sesame oil. Add a bay leaf and somewhere between 1—3 teaspoons crushed red pepper (chilli flakes) and a pinch of cayenne, if you like. It depends how hot you like your rancho sauce. This hot chili option is just what I happen to have in the kitchen right now. Let it get real hot. So the flakes are close to getting blackened. Then carefully pour in the red sauce. It will sear on the way in. With the oil and chilies making a ring around. Let it do its thing for 30 seconds, then stir while it quickly starts to boil. Turn down the heat, season with salt and pepper, put the lid on and let simmer for a while.

Preheat the oven to 350°F (180°C).

Make the egg batter by cracking the eggs into a bowl. Add some flour—in my case I used 1½ oz of gluten-free oat flour and ½ oz of potato flour. Add the milk. I only had cream at home so I diluted it a tad with water. Usually I use homemade nut milk. Add some salt and pepper. Stir it up.

Next oil up a 9 x 16 inch (23 x 40.5 cm)—or whatever you have— casserole pan. Put down a layer of opened-up and flattened peppers. There can be a little space around each; it's not necessary to be too tight. Add a bit of crumbled <u>queso</u> on top. Repeat the peppers and <u>queso</u> layers until you are out of ingredients. Pour on the egg batter, making sure to evenly-ish cover the whole top, and put in the oven for 25 minutes. You will know it's done when bits get golden and a little brown. Take it out and let cool. It will flatten a tad.

Serve a square on a plate with a generous large cooking spoon's-worth of the thickened red sauce on top.

Johanna and I also whipped up a green salad of baby spinach, chopped cilantro (coriander), chopped red cabbage and spoon-chunked avocado (like they do at <u>taquerías</u>). For the dressing we used olive oil, Champagne vinegar, a squeezed tangerine, salt and pepper. But as I write this, I realized that I spaced and that a dusting of chili powder would have been a nice finishing touch.

Enjoy, Chris

BOSS COOKIES
///////////////////////
Makes 40

In the 1980s my parents had a bakery called Boss Cakes. The entire
business was based on a carrot cake recipe by my Aunt Amy. These
lemon rosemary cookies are based on one of her recipes as well.

1 cup unsalted butter, softened overnight

2 egg yolks

½ cup sugar

2 teaspoons vanilla extract

2 tablespoons grated lemon zest (as much as you can bear grating
without getting too bored. I used half of a Buddha's hand lemon)

1¼ tablespoons finely chopped rosemary leaves

potato starch and tapioca, for the work counter

1¼ cups almond flour (ground almonds)

¾ cup rice flour (ground rice), plus extra to dust

½ teaspoon baking powder

¼ teaspoon salt

In a stand mixer, cream the butter a little to soften it further,
then add the egg yolks, one at a time, the sugar and the vanilla,
and beat until lighter in color and creamy. You are supposed to
use a stand mixer fitted with a paddle attachment for this recipe.
If you don't have one, use an electric beater or a wooden spoon
and a mixing bowl. Really do beat it until it gets lighter colored,
though. Beat in the lemon zest and rosemary. Sift in, or just put
in, the dry ingredients, and you might as well combine it with
your hands, just until blended. Don't overwork.

Flour a work counter—I like to use potato starch and tapioca for
that—and form maybe 4 dough tubes, rolling them into shape with
your hands. Wrap these in parchment (baking) paper and refrigerate
for a few hours.

Preheat the oven to 325°F (160°C). When the oven comes to
temperature take the dough out of the refrigerator, unwrap it
and thriftily lay that parchment paper on a baking sheet or cookie
sheet. Slice each dough tube into 10 cookies about ½ inch (1 cm)
thick. Bake for 13 minutes—let them get as brown as you like.
Maybe set the timer for 13 minutes and then watch them. I like
kind-of-burned food myself.

Take them out of the oven, put the baking sheet on a cooling rack
or build some simple mechanism to allow the sheet to be suspended in
the air, like two books. Let the cookies cool for about 10 minutes.

Johanna

Here in Iceland we have an excellent food commodity that one could describe as 'the Champagne of meat'. It is rare, and raised under very special conditions, not to be found anywhere else. Icelandic lambs roam free in the highlands during the summer, feasting on herbs, mountain grass and crystal-clear stream water. Their short life is one of beauty. The farmers treat them well and talk about them with deep respect. My family has a farm in an area called Skaftártunga, which is a great sheep-raising area surrounded by volcanoes and glaciers and on the foothills of Iceland's enormous highlands. Sheep farming and herding has been the area's livelihood for 1,000 years.

Although we don't raise sheep ourselves, it is one of the responsibilities of my farm to shepherd the highlands in autumn (fall) with the other farmers in Skaftártunga. Through this lovely duty, shepherding has become my hobby. For one week in the autumn I go with around thirty people up into the highlands and round up the sheep in places with names like Evil Canyon and Black Mountains. Knowing how the animals are raised, treated and respected has filled me with adoration for this ancient industry.

Nowadays Icelandic lamb can be found in quality food markets around the world.

On the farm we love to put some lamb chops on the grill or, if the weather is bad, just slightly brown the meat in a pan and roast it in the oven. Here comes a simple dish of lamb that is just as classic as it gets.

Grilled Lamb Chops with Potatoes, Mushroom Sauce and Salad

Serves 4

1 kg potatoes
olive oil, for drizzling
8 lamb chops
(I recommend you ask the butcher
to cut you thick ones)
fresh thyme leaves
salt

For the mushroom sauce
2 tablespoons butter
400 g mushrooms, cleaned and finely chopped
fresh thyme leaves
1 teaspoon salt
100 ml red wine
200 ml double (heavy) cream

For the salad
1 pint cherry tomatoes, quartered
2 bunches of fresh salad greens
3 tablespoons olive oil
1 tablespoon basil vinegar
1 teaspoon Dijon mustard
1 teaspoon salt

Preheat the oven to 200°C (390°F). Cut the potatoes into wedges. Drizzle with olive oil and season with salt. Put in an ovenproof dish. Roast in the oven for about 40 minutes, or until crisp and golden.

When the potatoes are almost cooked, preheat the grill to high. Take the lamb chops, drizzle them with olive oil, sprinkle with thyme and season with salt. Grill them for 3–5 minutes on each side. Set aside and keep warm.

Meanwhile, heat the butter in a frying pan (skillet), add the mushrooms and fry with the thyme leaves until the mushrooms are tender. Add the salt, then add the red wine and simmer until the alcohol has evaporated. Add the cream and the resting juices from the meat, if you have some.

For the salad, toss the tomatoes with the salad greens in a large bowl. In a small bowl, mix the olive oil, vinegar, mustard and salt to make a salad dressing.

Serve with red wine and menthol cigarettes, and have a perfect evening!

Opposite: A Perfect Evening, 2021. Oil on canvas, 55 × 80 cm (21½ × 31½ inches).

GRILLED LAMB CHOPS WITH POTATOES, MUSHROOM SAUCE AND SALAD

```
M O C Z K A
- - - - - -
SERVES 2-4
FOR THE VEGETABLE-FISH BROTH:
1 whole carp or 2-3 carp heads
1 parsley root
1 parsnip
2 carrots
1 head celery, stalks only
125 g butter
plain (all-purpose) flour, enough to thicken

FOR THE GINGERBREAD SAUCE:
250-300 g gingerbread (not very sweet; you can always
  buy some ready-made in a health food store)
2 x 330 ml bottles dark beer
200-300 g almonds
150 g hazelnuts
150 g prunes (dried plums) or dried peaches
400 g raisins
juice of 3 big lemons, plus extra to season
3 tablespoons sugar or honey
1 pinch of salt
```

Put the carp and vegetables into a large pan, cover with cold water and cook, simmering like chicken soup, for 20-30 minutes. After cooking, strain the carp and vegetables through a sieve, discarding both. The broth must be transparent.

For the sauce, put the gingerbread into a bowl, pour over the dark beer and soak the gingerbread for 20-30 minutes, or until it is soft. Pass the mixture through a sieve or simply mix until smooth.

Finely chop the almonds, hazelnuts, prunes (dried plums) or peaches, and raisins. Mix in a bowl with the remaining ingredients, put in a pan over low heat and simmer for 30 minutes, until the consistency is like jam or pudding — a bit runnier but creamy.

Make a roux as for soup: melt the butter in a frying pan then add the flour and cook, stirring, until lightly golden brown. Mix the roux with the gingerbread sauce. Season to taste with lemon juice and salt.

The consistency is like jam or pudding with visible elements of dried nuts and fruit. It must be thick! This is one of those dishes that tastes better than it looks.

Moczka can be eaten cold or hot.

MINUCHIN PIE   Serves 6

Ingredient list

1 kg potatoes
4 eggs
4 cloves garlic
2 onions
1 red pepper
4 tablespoons olive oil
240 ml peeled tomatoes
100 g cubed bacon
500 g minced (ground) beef
salt and ½ tablespoon
   black pepper
1 tablespoon dried oregano
1 tablespoon ground cumin
3 tablespoons raisins
120 g pitted green olives, halved
½ teaspoon ground nutmeg
125 g butter
300 g spinach leaves
100 g mozzarella cheese, sliced
1 puff pastry sheet
parsley, to decorate

Directions

1 Wash, peel and boil the potatoes in a pan of salted water.
2 Boil 3 of the eggs in a pan of water for 10 minutes. Cool under running water, then peel and slice.
3 Dice half the garlic, 1 onion and the red pepper. Heat 3 tablespoons of the oil in a large pan over medium heat and sauté the vegetables for 5 minutes until browned. Next, add the tomatoes, bacon and minced (ground) beef, mashing with a fork to avoid lumps. Season with salt and the pepper, oregano and cumin. When the meat is almost cooked, add the raisins, olives and nutmeg. Turn off the heat and stir the mixture carefully, then set aside.
4 Mashed potatoes: Transfer the boiled potatoes to a large bowl, add the butter and mash with a fork to produce a chunky mash.
5 Spinach: slice the remaining onion, dice the remaining garlic, and sauté in a pan with the remaining oil. Allow to cool and then stir in the spinach.
6 Assemble the pie in a deep baking dish (30 × 20 × 6 cm/ 12 × 8 × 2 inches):
  a) First layer: mashed potato
  b) Second layer: spinach
  c) Third layer: mashed potato
  d) Fourth layer: minced beef topped with hard-boiled egg slices
  e) Fifth layer: mashed potato
  f) Sixth layer: mozzarella cheese
  g) Roll out the pastry sheet to just larger than the pie dish and cover the whole dish with it, then trim the edges to fit. Beat the remaining egg with a fork and brush a little over the pastry.

Final step

Place the baking dish in the oven at 220°C (425°F). Remember all the ingredients have been pre-cooked, so the pie does not need long in the oven (around 25 minutes). Remove the pie as soon as the pastry turns golden and decorate with parsley.

VANILLA CUSTARD

Makes about ½ litre

Custard is a traditional and cheap Polish dessert. In the 1970s, Natalia LL prepared it frequently for shooting photographs and films from the Consumer Art series.

Ingredients
½ litre milk
1 tablespoon butter
½ vanilla pod (bean)
3½ tablespoons sugar
2 egg yolks, beaten
2–3 tablespoons potato starch
   (depending on whether thicker or thinner custard is preferred)
preserves, fruit syrup, fruits or chocolate sauce, to serve

Method
Simmer two thirds of the milk with the butter and vanilla pod (bean) in a pan over low heat.

In a bowl, mix the rest of the milk with the sugar, egg yolks and potato starch.

Pour the contents of the bowl into the simmering milk over low heat, stirring constantly to prevent lumps from forming.

When the custard thickens, boil it slowly, stirring, for another 1–2 minutes, then remove from the heat. Remove and discard the vanilla pod. The custard can be served with preserves, fruit syrup, fruits or chocolate sauce.

Natalia LL's Consumer Art is one of the most frequently interpreted and distinctive works in Polish contemporary art. The artist herself is a neo-avant-garde legend – a forerunner of performance art, experimental film and video, active in the fields of photography, installation and sculpture. In the mid-1970s, Natalia LL attracted the attention of international critics; Consumer Art in 1976 featured on the cover of Flash Art magazine.

Consumer Art is an extensive photographic and film cycle developed over the course of three years (between 1972 and 1975). It depicts young women sensually licking bananas, wiener sausages, salted sticks, ears of corn and caressing them with their lips, as well as feasting on custard and jelly. The footage is varied – the majority of images are black and white and depict a single model in a tight frame, most often a blonde woman with a girlish appearance. Natalia LL also collaborated with a different model, a brunette who is often portrayed in wider shots with bare breasts. With her look and

Agnieszka Rayzacher is an art critic, curator and owner of lokal_30 gallery in Warsaw, a co-founder of Feminist Seminar.

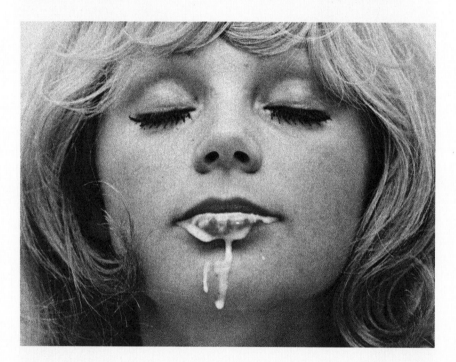

expression, her photographs and films take the representation of women and their erotic fantasies to a higher level.

Yet, the way the artist herself commented on her work is also of note: Natalia LL admitted that her initial idea consisted of a subversive mockery of Polish 'consumerism' in the realm of the 1970s, when even an ordinary wiener sausage was a dream come true. The use of the strategy and aesthetics of advertising photo shoots – images of young attractive women passionately licking bananas, sausages and salty sticks – in the context of socialist shoddiness and shortage economy appears as high-quality comic surrealism. Natalia LL once again proved to be an artist with a sense of humour and a penchant for depicting the ambivalent nature of things and phenomena.

On another note, we should evoke the artist's manifesto written in 1972, in which she declares: 'I record common and trivial events like eating, sleeping, copulation, resting, speaking, etc.'[1]. Consumer Art sits comfortably within the programme of permanent record and permanent formalization, which the artist pursued alongside Andrzej Lachowicz, Zbigniew Dłubak and Antoni Dzieduszycki in the PERMAFO group. Insofar as in Natalia LL's case, the 'cold' record of the act of consumption acquires sensual and gender-related connotations, we need to bear in mind the artist's origins in conceptual art and her declared abandonment of 'artistry' in favour of reality.

Finally, reflection on Consumer Art in the light of consumerism lends prominence to the question of commodification of the female body, addressed by the artist. Importantly, in Poland in the 1970s (as opposed to democratic countries), sexuality was absent from the public sphere. Thus, taking the lead in terms of sexuality by women can be understood as a gesture not devoid of

political undertones, even if it was understood merely by a narrow circle of viewers and its more comprehensive interpretation is possible only now. Owing to Natalia LL's artistic stance, her uncompromising and 'seductive' pieces that feature both distinctive and attractive visual form, the artist's output – particularly Consumer Art – provides a major point of reference and an inspiration for the next generations of artists.

Agnieszka Rayzacher

1 Natalia LL, Transformative Attitude, 1972, nataliall.com/en/transformative-attitude-1972/, accessed: 1 November 2020.

Let's Celebrate the Making of Trinidad Christmas Cake

INGREDIENTS

Serves 8–16

225 g (8 oz) sultanas (golden raisins)
225 g (8 oz) raisins
225 g (8 oz) currants
1 bottle (750 ml) dark rum
¼ bottle cherry brandy
¼ bottle port (optional)
225g (8 oz) soft brown sugar
225g (8 oz) unsalted butter, plus
    extra for greasing
6 free-range eggs
peeled rind of 1 lemon
225g (8 oz) plain (all-purpose) flour
½ teaspoon freshly grated nutmeg
2 teaspoons ground allspice
2 teaspoons ground cinnamon
½ teaspoon sea salt
2 teaspoons bicarbonate of soda
    (baking soda)
110 g (4 oz) glacé (candied) cherries,
    chopped
1 tablespoon browning
1 teaspoon vanilla essence
125 ml (4 fl oz) molasses

As an artist, poet and passionate cook, in terms of creativity, I see no fundamental difference between painting a picture, writing a poem or cooking a delicious meal. The only difference is in the use of materials. It is generally accepted that the process of creating art is energized by an impulse to bring together artistic elements for expressive impact. In the culinary arts, these elements are combinations of edible ingredients intended to produce a gastronomic delight that has an immediate effect on our five senses. I am convinced that the creative art of cooking and sharing food is a powerful means of spiritual and social bonding, of which the Trinidad Christmas cake is a perfect example.

The Cooking Instructions

Preparation:
Into a bowl of suitable size, put the washed dried fruits, to establish a heady relationship with three-quarters of the bottle of rum and the cherry brandy; go on, add the port if you are dying to. Be generous: give them 3–6 months in a covered bowl to really get to know each other. However, if you are in a hurry, overnight will also be fine.

Now for the browning: put 2 ample tablespoons of the sugar into a saucepan (preferably of cast iron) over medium heat. Heat the sugar, without stirring, until it becomes a bubbling caramel. Carefully add 150 ml (5 fl oz) water and stir it to a dark brown liquid. Set aside to cool.

1. Now you can begin to make the cake in earnest: for a really celebratory atmosphere, put on hot, hot calypso music, then in a mixing bowl of suitable size, cream the butter and the remaining sugar to a pale yellow, which indicates that the sugar and butter have dissolved into a happy understanding.

2. At this early stage, you could allow yourself a tiny shot of the remaining rum for the pleasure of the occasion. In a bowl, whisk rhythmically the eggs and lemon rind to a frothy disposition. Remove and discard the lemon rind and mix the frothy eggs, a little at a time, into the creamed butter and sugar mixture until it becomes smooth in consistency.

3. In a separate mixing bowl, combine the flour with the nutmeg, allspice, cinnamon, salt and bicarbonate of soda (baking soda). If you're dancing at this point, restrain yourself! In sequential order, a little at a time, gently fold into the egg-butter-sugar mixture: the flour and spice mixture, the drunken fruit, the glacé (candied) cherries, the browning, vanilla and molasses. Combine it all well and enjoy the heady bouquet of this rum-sodden mixture.

4. Preheat the oven to 150°C (300°F). Grease a 23 cm × 5 cm (9 × 2 inch) cake pan with butter and line the top and sides with baking (parchment) paper. Turn up the music, shake '*yuh body-line*'; this is a satisfying point in the cooking process. There before you is a cake mixture *to die for*. Pour the batter into the pan. Bake for 3 hours, or until testing with a skewer results in a clean withdrawal.

5. Gently heat the remaining rum. When hot, spoon it onto the still warm cake; it will happily soak in, with that great promise of transforming this Trinidad Christmas cake as it matures wrapped in foil, for up to 12 months, if you can wait that long, into an eating experience you'll never forget as long as you live.

Christmas Come-an-Gorn

Ageless Christmas ketch a piggy-back
from time, an he comin laden wid promises;
expectations thick in de air, There's no lack

of energy, people makin big-big commess
excited about Christmas. Charlotte Street
stores sellin lace curtain-cloth, doin business

like dey never done before. Soca beat
on the PA system Fada Christmas
wid a black face, pillow-stuffed belly, greet-

in everybody; he dress-up like ole mas;
but nevermine all-a-dat, is de food
ah waitin for: ah-lot-ah rum go pass

dese lips, ah go hit de Vat 19 good,
an before Christmas come an gorn
ah go get tight as everybody should.

Ah go eat Christmas cake meh mudder born
to make wid she special rum recipe.
She cookin through de night, den Christmas
mornin de house smell like food festivity:
boiled smoked ham, roasted turkey, rice-an-peas,
plenty sorrel, ginger beer and mauby,

an every Tom, Dick an Harry like bees
in de house jus like round ah sugar barrel.
Now, lemmeh wine meh body if yuh please.

SICILIAN PASTA WITH AUBERGINE

'Sicily, the "eternal garden of the Mediterranean", as it is called, is a unique combination of the cultural traits of the populations that have conquered the island in the past. This living blend of cultures is one of the great treasures of this land. It is expressed in the Sicilian lifestyle, which includes its famous cuisine and, in particular, its specialities made with aubergine (eggplant). This fruit has for centuries featured in popular legend, as a bizarre aphrodisiac. Meanwhile, the aubergine has conquered a significant place on the dining tables of Sicily, enlivening dishes from the refined to the simple and tasty, such as the following recipe for Sicilian pasta with aubergine.'

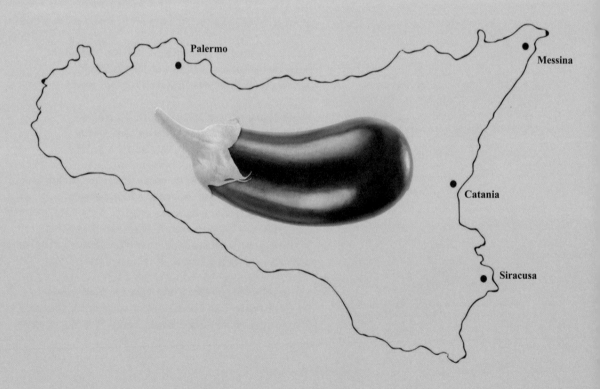

Palermo

Messina

Catania

Siracusa

MARE MEDITERRANEO

Serves 6

300 g (about 3 medium) aubergines (eggplants)
1 tablespoon rock salt (for soaking), plus extra to season
½ onion, finely chopped
180 ml extra virgin olive oil
1 small chilli (chile) pepper
1 clove garlic, finely chopped
250 g ripe tomatoes, chopped
500 g penne rigate (or any other kind of pasta, preferably short)
12 basil leaves
100 g Parmigiano Reggiano, grated
salt, to taste

Preparation:

A – **1)** Wash the aubergines (eggplants) and cut them into cubes.
2) Fill a large bowl with water then add the rock salt and the aubergine cubes, weighing the cubes down with a plate so they are submerged.
3) Leave to purge in the salt water for 1 hour. **4)** Drain the water, squeezing the aubergine pieces with your hands to remove their natural bitter juices.

Sauce:

B – **1)** Put the onion into a large non-stick pan with the oil and place over medium heat. **2)** Add the chilli (chile) pepper to the pan with the onion and gently cook, stirring. **3)** Remove the chilli after 1 minute.
4) Add the garlic to the pan, taking care not to burn the mixture.

C – **1)** When the onion and garlic are a golden yellow colour, add the aubergine cubes. Leave to cook for 15 minutes, stirring. **2)** Before adding the chopped tomatoes, test the aubergine to make sure it is cooked and tender. **3)** Add the tomatoes to the pan and cook for another 5 minutes. **4)** Check the sauce is good for salt and turn off the heat.

Pasta:

D – **1**) Meanwhile, bring a large pan of water to the boil. **2**) When the water is boiling, add the pasta and let it cook to your taste, or for the time indicated on the packaging. **3)** Drain the pasta. **4)** Plate the pasta and sauce and garnish with some fresh basil leaves and grated cheese to your taste. **5)** Your aubergine pasta dish is ready to be served.

Anna Maria Maiolino

Winter Solstice Fictional Entheogenic Supper

CHESTNUT AND MUSHROOM MASH

Serves 2

1 kg fresh wild chestnuts
2 medium wild butter boletes,
　or similar (such as porcini/ceps)
3 tablespoons rapeseed (canola) oil
flat-leaf parsley, chopped, to garnish

Using a sharp knife, make a small slice in the shell of each wild chestnut. Bring 1.5 litres water to the boil in a large pan, add the chestnuts and boil for 1 hour, topping up the water if required. Drain the chestnuts and leave to cool. When cool, press the purée out of the chestnut shells into a bowl.

Chop the mushrooms into bite-size pieces. Heat the oil in a pan and fry the mushrooms until golden. Reheat the chestnut purée and serve with the fried mushrooms on top. Garnish with parsley.

FROM THE WOODS
Butter boletes (*Butyriboletus appendiculatus*)
and wild chestnuts foraged from Sevenoaks.

All pictures taken by Haroon in the studio kitchen.

MAGICAL HOT DRINK

Serves 2

6 g magic seeds, ground
18 g magic leaves, chopped
100 ml distilled malt vinegar

Place all the ingredients into a cauldron
with 1 litre water and boil over an open fire
for 1 hour. Keep topping up with water.

DON'T TRY THIS TEA AT HOME
Magic seeds, magic leaves, water.

Winter Solstice Fictional Entheogenic Supper

SHELVES
Samantha Donnelly sculpture, oxidized San Pedro (*Echinopsis pachanoi*) and crystals in a glass jar and ceramic pot on Croquet Shelving by Michael Marriott.

FOUND TILES
Ceramic tiles by Aldo Donini and Lelo Cremonesi circa 1988
found on a farm in Santa Maria Della Versa, Italy.

Kedgeree

I believe that everyone knows that kedgeree is an Anglo-Indian dish from the days of the Raj. Initially eaten at breakfast, this versatile dish can be enjoyed hot or cold, as a side dish or an entrée, and is good for lunch or dinner. Traditionally it is made with haddock, but I prefer to use Alaska black cod for my recipe.

Serves 4

1. Two medium onions, one diced, one thinly sliced

2. Two or a little more tablespoons olive oil

3. Two heaping tablespoons of curry powder

4. Four large hard-boiled eggs, whites and yolks separated: dice the whites and finely chop the yolks with a bunch of Italian parsley

5. Two hundred and fifty grams of Alaska black cod

6. One and a half cups of long grain rice, boiled until tender and drained

7. Salt and pepper, to taste

8. Green salad, to serve

In a skillet (frying pan) over medium heat, sauté the thinly sliced onion well in the 2 tablespoons olive oil for about 5 minutes. When the onions are tender and starting to change color, remove them from the skillet and set aside. In the same skillet, heat a little more olive oil, if needed, and sauté the diced onion with the curry powder for 2 minutes then add the diced egg whites and Alaska black cod and cook gently for another 2 minutes.

Preheat the oven to 325°F (160°C). Put the cooked, drained rice in a large casserole (Dutch oven), add the curry mixture of diced onion, egg whites, and fish and mix well. Season with salt and pepper to taste, cover with the fried onion, then the finely chopped egg yolk and parsley mixture. Put the uncovered casserole into the oven and let the kedgeree cook for 20 minutes until heated through. Serve with a green salad.

Michael Morris

Miss General Idea, 1971–84

RAVIOLI ALL' UOVO

Serves 6–8

Dough for the ravioli:
······································
300 g 00 flour
200 g durum wheat semolina,
   plus extra to dust
2 eggs and about 6 egg yolks
a tiny quantity of olive oil

**For the ricotta cream border
inside the ravioli:**
······································
500 g fresh ricotta
45 g Parmesan cheese, grated
½ teaspoon freshly grated nutmeg

For the ravioli:
······································
18 egg yolks to be placed inside
   the ravioli

For the sage butter:
······································
60 g butter
6–8 sage leaves
sea salt, to taste

To serve:
······································
a couple of white truffles from
   Piemonte

My suggestion of wine is:
······································
Angelo Gaja Sorì San Lorenzo 2007,
   Langhe–Barbaresco, Italy

For dessert:
······································
A guava tart tatin prepared
   by Malu Barretto, my wife

I first mix and knead the ingredients for
the dough in a large bowl until uniform
and smooth. I then let the dough rest for
one hour before using it.

I place the ricotta on a paper towel to
remove excess water, then mix it in a bowl
with the Parmesan and nutmeg.

I roll out the ravioli dough to about 2 mm
(¹⁄₁₆ inch) thick and, using a 10-cm (4-inch)
cookie cutter, I make 36 circles. In the
centre of half of the circles I place a second
dough circle measuring 5 cm (2 inches) in
diameter (I cut 18 of these) and surround
it with a very thin and light ricotta cream,
which will hold the yolk in place. The
egg yolks are separated from the whites
by hand and each one is carefully placed
on the dough circles inside the ricotta
surround. Each ravioli holds one egg yolk.

After placing the yolk, I wet the borders
of the circles, place the remaining 10-cm
(4-inch) circles on top, and carefully press
the borders to create a tightly closed
ravioli. I then place each finished ravioli
in a semolina-dusted pan or tray.

While making the ravioli, I bring a large
pan of water to boil and very carefully I
place no more than 4 ravioli at a time in
the boiling water. I recommend a cooking
time of 3 minutes. It is very important
that the yolks remain whole throughout
the process. I carefully remove each
cooked ravioli using a slotted spoon,
transfer them to a plate and keep them
warm while I cook the others.

For the sage butter, I melt the butter in a
pan over low heat, add the sage leaves and
a pinch of salt and fry for 5–10 minutes.

Place 2–3 ravioli on each plate, top with
the sage butter and shave as much white
truffle as you can afford on top.

Still Life with Fish, after Pablo Picasso, 2020. Mixed media, 91.4 × 108.6 cm (36 × 42¾ inches).

Still Life with Guitar, after Juan Gris, 2020. Mixed media, 91.4 × 140.3 cm (36 × 55 inches).

Still life with Stone, after Pablo Picasso, 2020. Mixed media, 91.4 × 122.7 cm (36 × 48.3 inches).

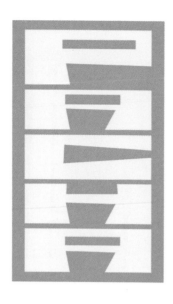

Pachamanca—The Northern Soul Remix
by Eamon Ore-Giron
Quechua: pacha (earth), *manka* (pot)

Serves 10–20

I think of this dish as more than food; it is a celebration of the earth, its bounty, and of family and friends.

The version pictured here is what my brother, sister, and I consider our northern remix of the original Peruvian *pachamanca*. *Pachamanca* is prepared in an underground oven, a hole dug in the ground lined with hot stones. The ingredients—the different foods in the dish—are placed in the oven in layers and cooked together. After digging a hole in the ground, you heat stones on a fire. The hot stones are positioned along the bottom of the hole and interspersed among the layers of food, which are traditionally topped with fava (broad) beans. A cloth is placed over the food and stones, and a layer of earth covers the cloth.

A traditional *pachamanca* will almost always include *humitas*, which are similar to Mexican tamales. The use of *huacatay*, an Andean mint, is also common. In this remix, we don't add *humitas*, and instead of *huacatay* we use rosemary and sage, which reflect the flavors of North America. We also use chimichurri sauce—fresh flat-leaf parsley, garlic, olive oil, lemon, salt and pepper all blended together—as a garnish for the dish instead of a typical Peruvian sauce called *japchi*, which is made with Rocoto pepper, cilantro (coriander), fresh cheese, and parsley.

I've left this recipe intentionally open to encourage you to experiment. Marinate your meats however you like,

or go without meat! We marinate our meat in beer and rub our chicken with butter. Try using all kinds of spices and add any kind of vegetable you like. We use lots of squashes and tubers. We soak corn in brine and cook it in the husk. We wrap green beans in cheese-cloth (muslin) and leave them wet from washing so they steam while cooking.

Suggested Ingredients:
· Meat: beef (roast), chicken, lamb, pork loin (with fat); can be wrapped in a banana leaf
· Vegetables: potatoes, yams, sweet potatoes, sweetcorn, onions, carrots, beets (beetroot), fava (broad) beans, green beans, squash (any larger variety, like acorn)
· Herb and spices: rosemary, sage, thyme, cumin

Important Information:
· Volcanic rock is best, or other stones that have <u>no</u> humidity (stones with any moisture will explode).
· Heat stones over a strong flame for an hour.
· In the photos, you'll see that we lined the hole with bricks. If you're digging a temporary hole and only using stones, first place the hot stones at the bottom; that will be your oven's floor.
· Place food in the center of your stone floor and build another layer of stones over and around the food. Repeat this until you have a pyramid of food covered by hot stones.
· We soak alfalfa hay in water for a while before placing it on top of the layers in lieu of fava (broad) beans.
· Cooking time is usually 1½ to 2 hours. You can't check how things are coming along, and it's better to be patient than to take things out early. The good thing is that this method of cooking involves very little oxygen, so the threat of burning is minimal.

make fire and heat stones

the spread

first layers: hot stones and tubers

more stones

place meat fat-side up

chicken and more stones

place herbs

place squashes

more stones and beets

173

carrots and more stones

corn

more corn and green beans

cover with wet alfalfa hay

cover with canvas or tarpaulin

cover with earth

put the kids to work

blessing to four directions

offer *pachamanca un trago* (a sip)

let it cook

go and dance

after 1½ hours, it's safe to uncover

enjoy steam-bath

smell the alfalfa hay

take the food out

place on large dishes

serve and eat!

clean-up crew

THE ART OF GOOD TASTE

During FESMAN III (Festival Mondial des Arts Nègres) in Dakar in 2010, I sat down to lunch with five senior Black artists and asked, 'Who of you can cook?' There was a lot of laughter and a unanimous reply of, 'You can't be a good artist if you can't cook...'.

My father, filmmaker and photographer Horace Ové, always enthused over the art of cooking and fusing cuisines together. He learned to cook like many, through the osmosis of being in the family kitchen, picking up styles and techniques that suited his repertoire. Interestingly, all the men I know from Trinidad can cook; it's just something everyone does with pride.

I learned to cook with my father, side by side in our kitchen in West Hampstead, London in the mid-1970s, talking about everything and anything, with the conversation usually turning to discussions about Horace's youth growing up in Trinidad, carnivals, history, politics and family. He enjoyed recounting special occasions and remembering who cooked what, how they had cooked it and what was good about it.

Horace, being a documenter, had an obsession with the history of his culture, and the influences of the merging cultures and traditions of Trinidad, an overlap that also takes place in its food. Food becomes a huge part of identity and, as is the case with oral traditions, if not kept alive and passed on, that power of identity is lost and recipes disappear. The retaining process, the cooking itself, is remembrance. The ritual of cooking together with my father brought me closer to my family history, and in many ways food was my rite of passage to a culture at a distance.

With Horace now suffering from Alzheimer's disease, I'm grateful for all that he passed on to me, and I now realize how easily identity can be lost. I hope my daughter will, in the future, want to return home to eat my food, as I did my father's, and that the meals we share together become a continuance of that history; that the familiarity of smells and warmth that cooking and eating together brings will continue our tradition of Trinidadian cooking and that of our forebears.

— Zak Ové

PONCHE A CRÊME / BUJJOL / CALLALOO / CHICKEN ROTI

PONCHE A CRÈME

Traditionally this drink is served at Christmastime, but quite honestly it is delicious at any time.

Serves 6

6 eggs
grated zest of 1 lime
3 × 14-oz cans condensed milk
¾ × 14-oz can evaporated milk
1¼ cups dark rum
Angostura bitters, to taste
freshly grated nutmeg, to taste,
  to serve

Preparation:

In a large bowl beat the eggs and lime zest until they become light and fluffy. Gradually pour in the condensed milk while continuing to mix, then add the evaporated milk. Lastly add the rum and a dash or two of Angostura bitters to taste. Pour it into a bottle and chill in the fridge.

Serve over crushed ice with a sprinkling of freshly grated nutmeg. Be sure to make enough as everyone loves to have at least two glasses!

BULJOL

This is one of those dishes in which the quantity of ingredients is very much up to the cook's taste and preference. I usually use one piece of salt cod and then enough of the rest of the ingredients to make a colourful blended mix; it should be juicy and fresh.

Buljol is usually eaten for breakfast and it is traditionally served with fried or coconut bakes.

Serves 4

1 x 8-oz piece salt cod, soaked overnight
    in warm water
4–5 tomatoes
½ English cucumber
bell pepper (any colour), halved and seeded
spring onions (scallions)
olive oil
black pepper
squeeze of lime juice
1 Scotch bonnet chilli, finely chopped
    (optional) or hot pepper sauce, to serve

Preparation:

Put the soaked, drained salt cod into a pan, cover with water, bring to a boil and cook for about 5 minutes to remove the salt.

Drain, rinse and taste the fish. If it is still too salty repeat the boiling/draining process until satisfied, then flake the fish into small pieces and put into a serving bowl.

Dice all the vegetables into small pieces to make a dish with even-sized pieces that are easy to hold on a fork. Add the chopped vegetables to the fish, then mix in olive oil and black pepper to taste and a squeeze of lime juice.

You can add some finely chopped Scotch bonnet to the mixture or serve with hot pepper sauce on the side.

CALLALOO

Serves 4

2 tablespoons olive oil
1 onion, chopped
1 tablespoon minced garlic
1 medium sweet pepper (any colour is fine), chopped
12–16 okra, chopped
½ cup finely chopped pimento (or sweet pepper)
½ cup peeled, seeded, and finely chopped pumpkin
1 bundle dasheen leaves (not too much stem), washed and chopped (or you can use a mix of baby and large spinach – about 2 bags)
1 cup vegetable stock (broth)
2 × 14-fl oz cans coconut milk
salt, to taste
Scotch bonnet chilli (left whole) for flavour (you can add hot pepper sauce after cooking to taste)

Preparation:

Heat the olive oil in a large pan over a medium heat, add the onion, garlic and pepper and sauté for a few minutes untill the onion is translucent (do not fry). Add the okra, pimento (or sweet pepper), pumpkin, dasheen leaves, stock (broth) and coconut milk then stir everything together and season to taste with salt. Let it reach boiling point, then lower the heat and add the Scotch bonnet chilli, but do not allow it to burst (it will then be far too hot to eat).

With the heat on low, allow it to simmer with the lid on for about 30 minutes, stirring occasionally until all the ingredients combine and become soft. Remove from the heat, remove and discard the Scotch bonnet chilli and put the remaining contents into a blender. Blend to make a smooth soup, but not so smooth as to lose all texture.

CHICKEN ROTI

Serves 4

2 lb boneless chicken thighs
2 tablespoons chopped cilantro (coriander)
roti, to serve

For the marinade
3 cloves garlic, finely chopped
½-inch (1-cm) piece fresh ginger, chopped
1 tablespoon curry powder
½ cup of cilantro (coriander) leaves
⅓ Scotch Bonnet chilli (or milder chilli
  pepper if you prefer less heat)
2 tablespoons olive oil
2 teaspoons salt (or to taste)

For the sauce
4 tablespoons olive oil
½-inch (1-cm) piece fresh ginger,
  finely chopped
3 cloves garlic, finely chopped
1 small white onion, chopped
1 tablespoon curry powder
1 × 14-oz can garbanzo beans (chickpeas),
drained and rinsed
2 potatoes, boiled and cut into cubes
2 cups coconut milk
2 cups chicken stock (broth)
salt and pepper, to taste

Preparation:

For the marinade: put all the ingredients in a large bowl and mix together (or blend in a blender if you like a smooth paste). Mix the chicken into the marinade, cover with plastic wrap (cling film) and let it sit in the fridge for at least 30 minutes.

For the sauce, heat a deep skillet or frying pan over a medium heat and, when hot, add half the olive oil, then fry the marinated chicken thighs skin-side down first for 7–8 minutes per side or until cooked through and crispy on the outside. Remove the chicken from the pan, leaving the juices and bits in the pan, and transfer to a plate. Add the remaining olive oil, the ginger, garlic and onion and cook for about 5 minutes, stirring, until the onion is translucent. Add the curry powder and cook, stirring, for 1 minute until fragrant.

Add the remaining sauce ingredients, season with salt and pepper, turn down the heat to low and let it simmer uncovered for 10–20 minutes. Cut the chicken into bite-size pieces and stir into the sauce. Cook for 5 minutes. Top with cilantro (coriander).

Wrap it all up in a roti to serve.

OVEN-BAKED SHKODRA-STYLE CARP

Serves 6

Carp are fish that live in both fresh water and salt water. The species that lives in Lake Shkodra, the largest lake in the Balkans, has a distinctive flavour, and is best suited to this traditional Albanian dish.

Carp are 80 cm to 1.3 m (2½ to 4¼ feet) long. The spawning season runs from early March to early summer. It is fished near the shore and the finest part of this fish is its head.

INGREDIENTS

- 3–4 kg fresh carp
- 400 ml olive or sunflower oil
- 1.5 kg white or yellow onions
- 1.5 kg fresh tomatoes or 700 g tomato passata (puree)
- 40 g garlic cloves
- 150 ml white wine vinegar
- 6–8 pitted prunes (dried plums), to taste
- 8–9 fresh or dried bay leaves
- 20–30 g (1 tablespoon) caster (superfine) sugar
- salt and pepper, to taste
- Albanian cornbread, toasted, to serve
- a glass of white or red wine, to serve

METHOD

1. Scale and gut the fish, taking care to also remove the triangular-shaped bone located in the head (it can give the fish a bitter taste). Once gutted, cut the fish into 2–3-cm (¾–1¼-inch) thick slices.
2. Heat the oil in a large frying pan. When hot, add the fish slices and fry for 2–3 minutes per side. Remove the fish from the pan and set aside. Keep the oil in the pan to make the sauce.
3. Slice the onions lengthwise. Add them to the pan, turn the heat to low, and brown the onions, stirring, for 40 minutes, adding a little water from time to time.
4. Peel and dice the fresh tomatoes, if using. Add the diced tomatoes (or tomato passata/puree, if using) and the garlic cloves, chopped in half, to the browned onions.
5. Then add the salt and pepper, wine vinegar, prunes (dried plums), bay leaves and sugar. Stir from time to time on a low heat. When the sauce is reduced and starts to resemble a glaze, turn the heat off and leave to rest for 4–5 minutes.
6. Preheat the oven to 200 °C (390 °F). Place the carp slices in a baking dish, not too close together. Pour the sauce over the fish, add 300 ml of cold water and bake in the oven for 40–45 minutes, turning halfway through. The fish is ready when it is browned on both sides and the slices are well coated in sauce.
7. Serve the carp hot with some toasted traditional Albanian cornbread and a glass of white or red wine.

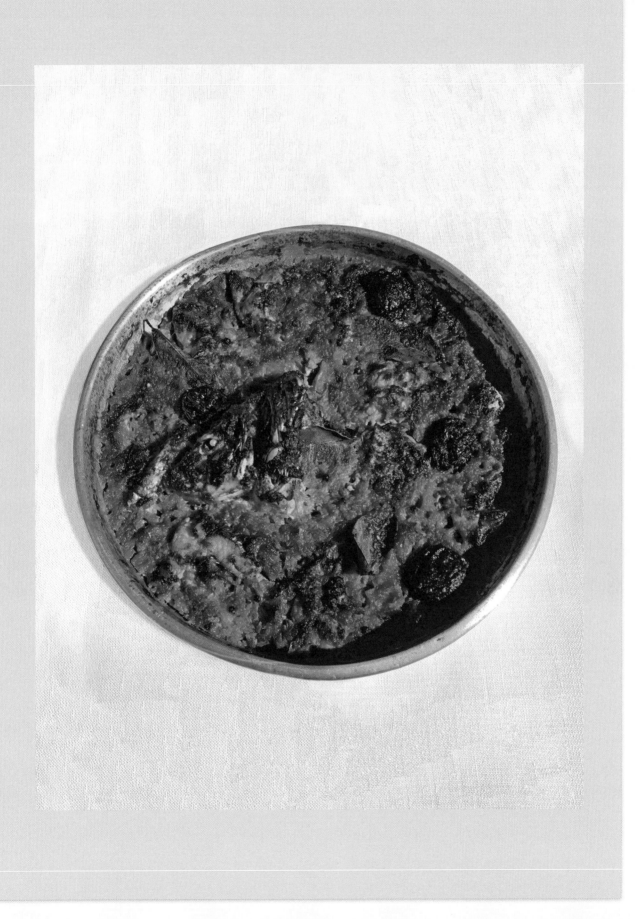

OVEN-BAKED SHKODRA-STYLE CARP

MARYSA MEDINA PARRENO'S PAELLA

Two cherries:
- choose a sunny afternoon in July
- walk around the countryside
  and look for a cherry tree
- find two burgundy color cherries
  and pick them from the tree
- eat one after the other and keep the
  stone in your mouth
- spit the stone as far as you can

Rainbow Carrots with Pickled Carrot Greens, Caramelized Shallots and Orange-cardamom Gel

Serves 10 as an appetizer

Orange-cardamom gel
300 ml orange juice
2 teaspoons agar powder
5 green cardamom pods, toasted
   then ground
a pinch of salt

Carrots and greens
250 g rainbow carrots, with greens
1 tablespoon salt, plus extra to sprinkle
250 ml water

250 ml white wine vinegar
2 tablespoons sugar
1 tablespoon salt

Caramelized shallots
150 g shallots
2 tablespoons olive oil
2 teaspoons sugar
salt, to taste

To garnish
50 g onion micro-greens

For the orange-cardamon gel, mix the orange juice with the agar powder, ground cardamom and salt in a pot over medium heat. Stirring, bring up to a boil. Let boil for 2–3 minutes, then transfer the mixture to a 23 x 17-cm (9 x 7-inch) rectangular dish, large enough to have a layer of juice about 1 cm (½ inch) deep. Put the dish into the fridge to set, at least 4 hours. When the gel has set, slice into 1-cm (½-inch) cubes. This will yield plenty of extra gel, in case necessary.

For the carrots and greens, separate the greens from the rainbow carrots and set them aside. Thinly slice the carrots on the bias using a mandoline. They should be about 3 mm (⅛ inch) thick. Put them in a bowl, sprinkle with salt, then set them aside.

To pickle the carrot greens, bring the water, vinegar, sugar and salt to a boil and turn off the heat. Put the leaves into a heatproof bowl. Pour the hot mixture over the leaves and let them steep for about 5 minutes. Remove from the vinegar mixture and let drain and cool.

For the caramelized shallots, thinly slice the shallots. Heat the olive oil in a non-stick pan on medium-low heat. Sprinkle the sugar all over the base of the pan. Add the shallots and let them caramelize lightly, 7–8 minutes.

When everything is set and cooled down, serve: take one slice of carrot, top it with a small amount of pickled greens, a cube of orange-cardamom gel, a couple of rings of caramelized shallot and onion micro-greens.

LUIZA PRADO DE O. MARTINS

RAINBOW CARROTS WITH PICKLED CARROT GREENS, CARAMELIZED SHALLOTS AND ORANGE-CARDAMOM GEL

The Wantee Tea

Makes 1 litre

80 per cent Earl Grey tea
+ 20 per cent gin +
5 tablespoons honey + fresh
juice of 2 lemons

'Wantee', 2013, Installation view
at Schwitters in Britain, Tate Britain,
London, 2013.

Betty
Drunk
Vodka

Vodka with squid ink,
according to your taste.

'Squid Ink Bar', Installation view at
the wet wet wanderer, Witte De With,
Rotterdam, 2017.

BASRA KISS

SERVES 2

Basra date syrup is produced in Basra, Iraq. In an effort to circumvent the 1990 UN Security Council sanctions on Iraq and sell their produce to western markets, the manufacturer lists the Netherlands as the country of origin.

This practice continues today, with multiple Iraqi brands bearing different locations of origin, even after the UN sanctions were lifted in 2003. As many US-based importers attest, high shipping charges to bring anything out of Iraq, as well as severe trade regulations applied to incoming packages from the region—including security scans and the resulting charges for holding shipments in port to enable these searches—have made it cost-prohibitive to import goods bearing the label 'Product of Iraq'.

Basra Kiss is a sandwich I developed for the Whitechapel Refectory at London's Whitechapel Gallery in 2019.

TO MAKE IT, YOU WILL NEED:

* 2 tablespoons of date syrup
* 2 tablespoons of tahini
* butter or oil, for frying
* 4 slices of halloumi or Akkawi cheese (a type of white brined cheese)
1 large piece of pita or lavash bread, about 10 inches (25 cm) in diameter
* ¼ cup chopped fresh mint leaves

In a bowl, mix the date syrup and tahini with a spoon. Admire the psychedelic swirls it makes when it begins to blend. In Iraq, this mixture is called *dibis wa'rashi*.

Heat a little butter or oil in a pan over a medium heat. Add the halloumi or Akkawi cheese and fry, turning once, until both sides are sienna brown. Remove from the pan and transfer to a plate.

Next, spread the date syrup and tahini mixture on the pita or lavash and place in the pan, over a medium heat. Arrange the toasted cheese evenly on top of the date syrup/tahini, then finish with a scattering of the mint.

Carefully roll and close the pita up like a burrito, or fold it over like a quesadilla. Be sure to continue to cook for a few minutes more, pressing down on each side using a spatula, like a pressed sandwich.

Finally, think deeply about the origin of things, like words. Hospitality is derived from hospes, meaning "host", "guest," or "stranger." Hospes is formed from hostis, which also means "stranger" or "enemy," and is where words like "hostile" come from. We know where the date syrup in this recipe comes from, but where does this book come from? Is the host of this recipe hostile? Is the publisher of this book hostile? Does the ink forming these letters, which form these words, derive from the blood spilled in a public square in Baghdad in 2007?

Cut in half and share.

Recipes are, of course, unnecessary. You cook by cooking with people. Something I like to do is get a bunch of people together and make a stew out of whatever ingredients, techniques, and family methods the group has to hand. This never fails to be delicious, and never leaves a repeatable recipe. But I'm going to give you three recipes, because I've been asked to. A note: for the fish recipes it's extremely important that you use trash fish. What is trash fish? Fish that is plentiful and wild, often small, the kind of fish a fisherperson will roll up to the dock with in Karachi Harbor, Providence, or Trouville-sur-Mer. Mackerel, flounder, sea robin, sardine, herring, striper, bluefish: these are all trash fish.

KHICHRI
Serves 4–6

Akbar the Great (the Mughal emperor and poet who blended Muslim and Hindu culture) used to feed this to his elephants. For humans, it's an extremely soothing, very healthy and proteinaceous dish of rice and lentils with onions fried in plenty of butter or oil, and whole spices like black cardamom, clove, and bay leaf.

You start by taking 1½ cups (any kind of cup!) of (the longest grain) basmati rice and ½ a cup of (orange) red lentils (*masur dal*) and washing it in a bowl, letting it soak. Meanwhile, fry a sliced small onion in plenty of butter or oil until the edges are dark brown. Now combine with the drained rice and lentils in a pot, and add 3¾ cups (same cup as you used before) of water, some black peppercorns (preferably from Tellicherry), 3 black cardamoms, 2 bay leaves, and 4–6 little baseball-bat cloves. Bring this to the boil, then cover and simmer on the lowest heat for about 17 minutes. You eat this with keema, or yogurt and hot chutney, or chili or lime pickle, or whatever you want. Or feed it to a large pet.

CLAM CHOWDER
Serves 4–6

I love clam chowder because no one knows where it came from, and there's a recipe for it in *Moby-Dick* (which I once made with Paris-based French artist Philippe Parreno — it was very rich and kind of stodgy). They say it comes from the word *chaudière*, or hotpot, as used by French fishermen, but it's as American as they come. Jasper White (the Boston-based chowder chef) might dislike this recipe since it doesn't contain salt pork, one of the orthodox elements in New England chowder ingredients. Well, I developed this recipe while living with a pescatarian and used garlic and chili instead

(it works). Other points: you want potatoes that are starchy, not waxy, because the starch helps thicken the broth. Second, sourdough bread and seafood broth is a hellishly good combination, so find a good sourdough loaf. Finally, my other innovation on the classic method is to remove the clams after cooking and replace them at the end, thus avoiding rubbery-clam syndrome. If you have very large clams (like big quahogs), chop them up roughly prior to putting them back in the soup, though you then lose the sensual quality of perfectly tender, whole clams in your soup.

Warm a large knob of butter and 2 tablespoons of olive oil in a heavy soup pot over medium-low heat. Chop 2 cloves of garlic and add to the pot, with ½ a teaspoon of crushed red pepper (chilli flakes) and ½ teaspoon of peppercorns. Add 1 diced large onion and sweat until translucent and flimsy but not browned. Add 1 kg (maybe 24 medium) clams and a cup of water (or white wine), turn the heat to high and cover with the lid. Take off the lid after five minutes and check that all the clams have opened (littlenecks can be a bit reticent; sometimes you have to turn them right-side up to get them to open). Using a slotted spoon, transfer the open clams to a bowl (discard any clams that refuse to open).

Now cut 3 large starchy potatoes into cubes and add to the pot with enough water to cover them. Salt generously to avoid stirring too much later. (Meanwhile remove the clam meat from their shells and discard the shells.) Boil the potatoes until they are well cooked and tender enough to eat. Crush one or two of the potato cubes into the broth to thicken it a bit. Add 1 lb or ½ kg of trash fish fillets (flounder is perfect) and cook them in the broth just until they flake apart (2–3 minutes). Turn the heat off, throw in the clams and any residual broth from their bowl, half a bunch of chopped parsley, and enough cream to thicken the broth. Ladle into bowls, and add toasted sourdough bread, either in slices or as croutons.

FISH STEW
Serves 8

This is my version of *bouillabaisse*, with some help from the fish stew of Liguria. Following the French system of bestowing appellations, I do not call my stew "bouillabaisse," because the particular fishes required to make a proper one are unavailable in New York (particularly the legendarily bony *rascasse*, or scorpionfish, without which no authentic bouillabaisse can be made—read A. J. Liebling's 1962 article "The Soul of Bouillabaisse Town," on *The New Yorker* website). Instead I have developed a retinue of seafood found in this area, which together produce a stock of similar complexity. What's important is to use a bony fish like a gurnard (a type of bottom-feeding fish similar to the *rascasse*)—I use the cool and ugly sea robin, a trash fish I buy for $1.50 a pound. I fillet the fishes myself, but you can also have the fishmonger do it and ask to keep the carcasses. This is a good dish for a special occasion, when you have friends helping and drinking a bottle of Bandol or Juliénas with you in the kitchen. A fish stew is an epic poem.

2 yellow onions, coarsely chopped
1 large bulb of fennel, chopped, eight leafy
    fronds reserved, to serve
6–8 stalks celery, chopped
8 cloves garlic, 6 minced and 2 halved
10 peppercorns
3 bay leaves
1 sea robin (from the gurnard family; or use the
    boniest sea fish you can find), whole
1 snapper, filleted, carcass reserved
1 bass, filleted, carcass reserved
1 cup mushrooms (optional)
1½ lb mussels, cleaned and de-bearded
half a bottle Italian dry white wine (nothing fancy –
    Pinot Grigio or Orvieto will do)
1½ lb very small clams (*vongole*) or cockles
8 langoustines, or 1 lb of the biggest, coolest shrimp
    (prawns) you can afford, unpeeled
3 lb medium-waxy potatoes (or use new potatoes),
    peeled and cubed
½ bunch parsley
3 tablespoons olive oil
crushed red pepper (chilli flakes), to taste
1 teaspoon saffron, preferably Iranian
2 x 28 oz cans whole tomatoes, preferably Italian
    such as San Marzano
1 loaf sourdough bread
2–3 lb fillets of very fresh wild striped bass, wild
    halibut, wild cod, or other large-flaked white fish
salt and pepper

In a large stockpot, put one third of the chopped onion, fennel, celery, minced garlic, and all the peppercorns, bay leaves, the sea robin and fish carcasses (you can add mushrooms, and I recommend you do). No salt. Cover with cold water. Bring to the boil, and break up the carcasses using a wooden spoon. Leave to simmer slowly.

Meanwhile, in a soup pot, put the mussels and 1 cup of the wine, cover with the lid and cook over high heat until steam escapes from the beneath the lid. Check that all the mussels are open (discard any that remain closed). Using a slotted spoon, transfer the mussels to a bowl. Remove half the mussels from their shells,

discarding the shells, and put the mussels on a large platter. Strain the liquid in the soup pot into the stockpot. Repeat the exact same process with the small clams or cockles, adding them to the platter too.

Put the langoustines or shrimp (prawns) into the stockpot (put them in a sieve, so they don't float away), and cook in the simmering stock until just done or slightly underdone (less than 1 minute). Remove and reserve. Boil the potatoes in a pan of salted water until just tender, then drain, and add to the platter. Finely chop the parsley and add to the platter.

Back to the stock. After 30 minutes elapses, strain the contents of the stock pot through a sieve into another pot. You have to really push (use the back of a spoon) to squeeze out all the flavor. Remove all solids from the sieve (after the fish carcasses cool, pick through them for meat, and use it to make fish cakes, a mayonnaise-based fish salad, or just a sandwich with hot sauce). Now strain the stock back into the stockpot, put it back over low heat and let it simmer, concentrating its flavor. It should smell pretty great.

Now the actual stew begins. In a heavy soup pot, heat the olive oil over medium heat and add the remaining chopped onion and fennel, cooking until translucent. Add the remaining minced garlic and crushed red pepper (chilli flakes) to your taste, and fry until the garlic is just off-white and the harshness of its aroma has been attenuated. Throw in the saffron and stir. Now add the tomatoes (but not their juices), breaking them up with a spoon. Cook this down over high heat until you have a mixture that's a little looser than tomato sauce, about 30 minutes. Now ladle in enough of the concentrated fish stock to make the right consistency and volume for your numbers and preferred thickness of soup and adjust the seasoning. Poach the snapper and bass fillets (used above, for their carcasses) in the stew and break them up a bit using a spoon.

Thickly slice and properly toast the sourdough bread, then quickly rub one side with the halved garlic cloves. Finally, slice the striped bass (or halibut or cod) fillet into 8 portions, one for each eater. Now poach the portioned fillets in the simmering stew broth. As soon as they're close to done, transfer each to a warmed soup plate. Now add the entire contents of the platter (mussels, cockles, potatoes, parsley) to the stew, turn up the heat, and heat as fast as you can. When back to the boil, add the langoustines or shrimp (reserving one to top each plate), count to fifteen, and ladle the stew over the fish fillets in each bowl, placing a langoustine on top, and add half a ladle of the fish stock to moisten if necessary. Prettily place a fennel frond on top of each bowl (lying down, not jutting out!) and wedge a slice of garlic-rubbed toast halfway into the soup on the side of each plate.

GINGER CHICKEN
Serves 4–6

Screw it, here's a fourth recipe, because I still have a little bit of space. Edna Lewis' book on country cooking—*The Taste of Country Cooking*—at the Southern idyll created by her family freed from enslavement is one of the best books to read to get a sense of when to cook things, at what season, and at what time of the week, the temporality of cooking being one of the most important things. In my family on Sundays we would cook this dish:

You cut a chicken into joints (go to YouTube if you don't know how, dummy). Fry the pieces in an entire cup of oil in a big pot or wok until golden. Remove. Now fry 2 sliced onions in this oil until deep golden brown and kind of sweet, then add 2 large handfuls of julienned fresh ginger (it is really a lot of ginger; this dish uses ginger as a vegetable, not a flavoring), let this soften in the oil, then return the chicken to the pot or wok, and add 4 medium-size sliced tomatoes. Let all this simmer on medium-low for an hour. Now add a sliced red bell pepper, and a few long green peppers, like the ones you see in Turkey, and let them cook another half hour or more, until the oil separates and the gravy is kind of thick and concentrated, and exceedingly flavorful and gingery. Add a bunch of chopped fresh cilantro (coriander) leaves and eat with a good roti.

MISO RAMEN
Serves 4

Fuck it, here's a fifth! Make a dashi broth out of kombu and bonito (look it up, it's easy). If you are not a vegetarian, also make a chicken broth by covering a whole chicken with water and simmering for four hours, with nothing else. Now combine these, half of each broth, and off the heat, stir in a teaspoon of very good miso per serving. Introduce 90 g of cooked somen or ramen-friendly noodles into each bowl, and ladle in enough broth to cover. Now add some chopped scallions (spring onions). That's it. It's extremely excellent. For the bells and whistles, you can add soy sauce-soaked soft-boiled eggs, and slices of pork belly, and some sautéed greens like chard or spinach, but the simple version is the one I like to have in the studio.

TOMATO CURRY
Serves 4

Damn it, here's a sixth, and this goes with the khichri, which was number one. Go back to the Ginger Chicken recipe and make it without the chicken. Just double the tomatoes, and add a teaspoon of cumin seeds to the oil at the beginning, and some dried red chili peppers (especially the cherry-shaped ones from Lahore if you can get them), and omit the long green peppers later. This is a very rich tomato curry that goes perfectly with any rice dish, or with bread and a Peshawari seekh kebab.

SCRAMBLED EGGS
Serves 3–4

Finally, a seventh. Scrambled eggs exist in every culture, and represent the basic units of cooking, the underlying grammar. Here's a good recipe:

Beat 6 eggs in a bowl. Heat a non-stick pan over medium heat and froth some butter in there—a pat if you fear butter, three pats if you don't. Spear a clove of garlic on a fork (yes!), and pour the beaten eggs into the pan. Trust me: slowly stir the eggs with the garlic-fork as curds form, moving the pan on and off the heat, until you have perfectly soft and wet scrambled eggs, with nice clouds of curds in an overall medium. Grind over some pepper and sprinkle over some salt (maybe a crunchy sea salt). The eggs will have an ethereal aroma, barely perceptible as garlic, but magical.

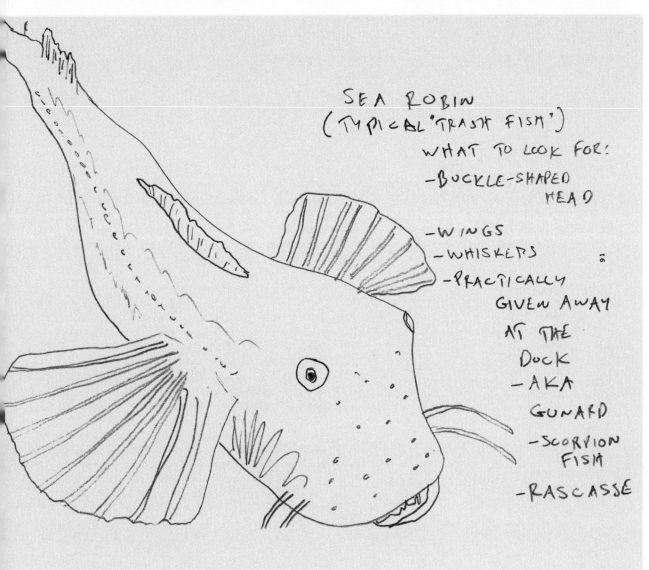

SEA ROBIN
(TYPICAL "TRASH FISH")
WHAT TO LOOK FOR:
- BUCKLE-SHAPED
HEAD

- WINGS
- WHISKERS
- PRACTICALLY
GIVEN AWAY
AT THE
DOCK
- AKA
GUNARD
- SCORPION
FISH
- RASCASSE

Grandma's Roast Pork with Mom's Dumplings and Warm Coleslaw

Serve the meat, dumplings and sauce on one plate and the coleslaw
in a little salad bowl on the side.

Serves about 10

Roast Pork

Preparation time: 30 minutes, cooking time:
   4½ hours (applies to roast pork only)

1.2 kg pork neck (in one piece, without bones)
1.5 kg fresh pork belly (side)
400 g onions
4 cloves garlic
1–2 tablespoons caraway seeds
salt

Cut the pork neck and belly (side) into 5–6-cm
(2–2½-inch) thick slices. Put the meat into a large
pan of cold water and bring to a boil over high heat.
Turn the heat to low, then simmer slowly for about
10 minutes. Pour away the water and rinse the meat
with cold water. Set aside. Dice the onions finely.
Cut the garlic into fine slices.

Preheat the oven to 180°C (350°F). Cook the meat
in a large pot with enough salted water to fully cover
the meat for 30 minutes, then take the meat out of
the pot (keep the water) and put it into a sheet pan.
Cover with the onions and garlic and add 100 ml or
so of the cooking water (the water should be at a
depth of 5 mm/¼ inch above the surface of the meat).
Cook in the oven for 10 minutes, then sprinkle with
the caraway seeds. Lower the temperature to 140°C
(280°F) and add another 250 ml of the cooking water.
Cook for 3½–4 hours. Take the meat out when it is
tender and the onions are golden brown. About 1 cm
(½ inch) of gravy should be left in the pan. If the meat
becomes too dry, add more cooking water. Serve with
the onions and gravy.

Dumplings

1.5 kg floury (baking) potatoes
about 600 g plain (all-purpose) flour (it depends
   on how much water the potatoes contain)
salt

Boil the floury (baking) potatoes in a pan of salted
water until tender, then peel and mash them using
a masher or potato ricer.

Add some salt and as much flour as necessary in
order to form 15–20 dumplings (5–7 cm/2–3 inches
in diameter) with light pressure. Do not knead the
potato dough.

Only add as much flour as necessary to create
a crumbly dough (similar to crumble dessert).
The finished perfect dumpling should be neither
waxy nor floury inside. (My Grandma's weren't
always the same either.)

Boil the dumplings in lightly boiling or simmering
water for 20–25 minutes. Take them out and poke
each dumpling to the centre with a meat fork in
order to create two evaporation holes. Serve hot.

Warm Coleslaw

1 white cabbage
50 g clarified butter
5 tablespoons vinegar
2 tablespoons sugar
2 teaspoons caraway seeds
250 g smoked bacon (white only)
salt and pepper

Cut the cabbage into quarters. Remove and discard the stalk and, using a large knife, cut into irregular thin strips 1–5 mm (1/16–1/4 inches) wide. Sweat the cabbage in a pot (use one with a lid) with some clarified butter then deglaze with some water (about 3 cm/1¼ inches high in the pot). Season with salt and add the vinegar, sugar and caraway seeds. Steam in the closed pot until done – about 60 minutes, or until the cabbage is just about soft.

Finely dice the bacon and fry in a separate pan until the fat has rendered and the bacon is golden brown.

Taste the cabbage and if necessary season to taste with salt, pepper and vinegar, then add the fried bacon and the hot rendered fat from the pan.

It should taste sweet, sour and smoky.

There is a name for the act of gathering what one can find naturally growing alongside the pathways of countryside: foraging. We mean plants, herbs and fruits that are not produced by farmers. Something edible that has not a legal owner (at least most of the time). // This food picking is typical of civilizations with a high percentage of wild terrain (hills, mountains, forests). Italy's Veneto region, where I was brought up, has been a poor area for a long time. People had a hard time scratching a living and foraging was a common source of food. // The dish *zuppa di quaresima* originally involved several wild pulses and spontaneous herbs, mostly provided through wandering around woods and fields. It's a masterpiece of simplicity and frugality. Like good Art should be (or is supposed to be) ... // Another well-known traditional recipe, *risotto con i bruscandoli* uses wild hops (a sort of common weed found in springtime), rosemary, sage, risotto rice and butter. There is actually a lot of rosemary in this risotto – it always reminds me of Joseph Beuys and of his passion for rosemary, both as an artist and a chef. // At the end of the day what artists do is very similar. In a nutshell, we collect raw cultural material (for free) and combine and mix it to create something new. It is a sort of cultural foraging. Somehow we are all gatherers.

Antonio Riello

QUARANTINE DRAWINGS
Antonio Riello's *Quarantine Drawings* are a very personal and tormented form of reportage of his kitchenscape. In February 2020 he started an obsessive reproduction of kitchen tools – humble sketches that, considered all together, might become an Alter-Modern 'Visual Dictionary'. This taxonomic classification reveals Riello's passion for Mark Dion researches: the main idea is to set an Anthropological Museum of culinary ergonomy and cruelty. The kitchen is, in fact, at the same time the famed place of domestic love, a sort of improvised scientific laboratory, a harsh kind of torture chamber. These 'object portraits' are, for sure, a form of testimony of a weird time, but they are also a devoted and oblique homage to Alberto Giacometti's drawing style.

All the works are made with ballpoint blue ink on simple paper (A3 size). The artist believes we need 'very ordinary' tools to be able to imagine 'extraordinary' adventures.

CONFINED TOOL 208, 2020. BLUE BALLPOINT PEN ON PAPER. 40 × 30 CM (15¾ × 11¾ INCHES)

MINESTRINA FORTUNATA

Serves 4
Preparation time: 2 minutes
Cooking time 15: minutes

This recipe belongs to my
maternal ancestors, people who
dwelt in the Eastern parts of
the Habsburg Empire and moved
during the eighteenth century to
Italy, to Milan. In the original
version, some hand-made thin-
sliced tagliatelle were boiled
for a few minutes in Jewish-
style chicken stock, in this case
enriched with small potatoes and
the flavour of locally available
fresh herbs. First the potatoes
were eaten. After that, the pasta
settled on the bottom of the plate
creating visual patterns that were
carefully interpreted following
a family fortune-teller tradition
(only good signs were able to be
reported, of course). After the
'reading' the rest of the minestra
was quickly eaten by the comforted
and uplifted diners.

My contemporary version is
suitable for vegans and better
suits a busy urban way of
life. It is perfect as comfort
food for dinner in winter.
Benign forecasting requires
a little domestic patience
and creative love.

2 sprigs of thyme
4 bay leaves
2 shallots
4 sage leaves
1 generous sprig of rosemary
2 teaspoons extra-virgin olive oil
240 g peeled new red potatoes, cut
   into 0.5 cm (¼ inch) cubes
1 litre vegetable stock (you can buy
   ready-made; there are pretty good
   products on the market)
200 g thin tagliatelle (known in
   Italy as *capelli d'angelo*; you can
   find it made with or without egg yolk)
1 pinch of saffron powder (gives a nice warm
   colour and works as a powerful antioxidant)

Put the thyme and bay leaves into
a steel tea infuser and close it
tightly. Finely chop the shallots,
sage leaves and rosemary and put
into a medium-large pot with the
olive oil. Warm over low heat,
stirring with a wooden spoon.
Add the diced potatoes and gently
let them cook for 3 minutes
until lightly gold. Pour in the
vegetable stock, turn the heat
up to high and bring to a rolling
boil. After 8–9 minutes of boiling
add the infuser with the herbs,
and the thin tagliatelle. It takes
about 2 minutes to cook. Turn off
the heat and remove the infuser.
Before serving, carefully stir
in the saffron powder.

CONFINED TOOL 198, 2020. BLUE BALLPOINT PEN ON PAPER. 40 × 30 CM (15¾ × 11¾ INCHES)

ZUPPA DI QUARESIMA

Serves 4
Preparation time: 7–8 minutes,
 plus overnight soaking
Cooking time: 30 minutes

A frugal soup from my paternal side (originally landed gentry who lived in Vicenza, not far from Palladio's La Rotonda), it was a popular dish for the Lent period, when meat was forbidden. Some people jokingly refer to it as 'cat soup' (*supa del gato*) implying that the greedy pet had stolen the meat from the kitchen table. Nowadays it could be considered a sort of Venetian-style ramen. A vegetarian zero-mile food, it is a prime example of a wise re-use of leftovers: proteins come from beans (usually a by-product of *pasta e fagioli*, or pasta and beans) and staple calories are provided by stale bread.

400 g dried borlotti beans

1.1 litres fresh cold water

2 bay leaves

1 carrot

4 slices of stale bread (not too thin)

4 teaspoons extra-virgin olive oil

4 free-range eggs

4 sprigs of fresh marjoram

salt and pepper

grated Parmesan, to serve

Put the dried beans into a bowl, cover with water and leave to soak for about 24 hours before using.

Preheat the oven to 120°C (250°F).

Drain and rinse the soaked beans well, put them into a large pot with the cold water and put over high heat. Add the bay leaves and the carrot.

Place a slice of bread on each of four soup plates. Season the bread with salt and pepper, drizzle with olive oil and put the plates in the oven to warm.

Bring the pot of water to a boil, cover with a lid and keep it over medium heat for 30 minutes. At this point remove and discard the carrot and the bay leaves. Remove the beans using a skimming ladle, put them into a bowl and cover them with a clean dish towel. Keep the water (now actually a bean stock) at a boil, with the lid on, turning the heat up to maximum.

Handling the soup plates carefully (beware of the hot temperature) ladle the very hot stock over the bread. Quickly crack 1 egg into each soup plate and around it spoon a generous portion of beans. Let the soup rest for 4–5 minutes until the eggs have a Bazotte-style consistency: a runny yolk and firm white.

Finally, before serving, add a marjoram sprig to each soup plate. At this stage many people love to cover the soup with a little avalanche of grated Parmesan; it might be the correct option.

CONFINED TOOL 29, 2020. BLUE BALLPOINT PEN ON PAPER. 40 × 30 CM (15¾ × 11¾ INCHES)

patriotic JELL-O® gelatin salad

Serves 12–14

This is a great salad to celebrate the Fourth of July.

For the blue layer

3-oz package raspberry
   gelatin dessert
1 cup hot water
1 can blueberries in juice, drained
   (reserve 1 cup juice)

For the white layer

1 × ¼-oz envelope
   unflavored gelatin
½ cup cold water
1 cup sugar
1 cup half-and-half (single) cream
1 teaspoon vanilla extract
2 cups sour cream

For the red layer

3-oz package strawberry
   gelatin dessert
2 cups hot water

For the blue layer, put the raspberry gelatin into a heatproof bowl with the hot water and stir to dissolve the gelatin. Add the reserved blueberry juice and refrigerate until partially set. Stir in the blueberries and pour into an 8-cup mold. Give the mold a little shake to remove any air bubbles, then place it in the refrigerator and leave to set.

Meanwhile, make the white layer. Put the unflavored gelatin into a bowl with the cold water and stir to dissolve the gelatin. Combine the sugar and cream in a pan, place over low heat and stir until the sugar dissolves and the mixture is almost about to boil. Remove from the heat, stir in the gelatin, then let cool. Once cool, mix in the vanilla and sour cream. Carefully pour it over the set first layer in the mold. Take care not to disturb the surface of the first layer. Return the mold to the refrigerator and leave to set.

Finally, for the red layer, put the strawberry gelatin into a heatproof bowl with the hot water and stir to dissolve the gelatin, then carefully pour over the set second layer. Return the mold to the refrigerator and leave to set completely.

When ready to serve, carefully unmold onto a cake board just larger than the width of the mold. Decorate with well-cleaned toy figurines or however you like.

FICTION HOUSE CHICKEN CURRY

I'm white like the Milky Bar Kid but
I'm Indian inside and you can bet a million quid.
I love the old movies like Kabhi Kabhi and
I know my aik, do, teen like my ABC

Super Gora. First verse

Fiction House was founded in Glasgow in 1997. It's a salon that on occasion doubles as an exhibition venue. At Fiction House (currently in Berlin) I serve the Fiction House Curry. In the spirit of a symposium, we drink wine, discuss whatever comes up and, once conversation has started flowing, the curry is served. It takes a moment or two to work its magic, and then the singing starts. The singsong is what I grew up with in a largely Irish immigrant household in the West of Scotland. The wandering German poet Johann Gottfried Seume observed, '*Wo man singt, da laß dich ruhig nieder, böse Menschen haben keine Lieder*' – 'Where there is singing, you can safely stay, for wicked people have no songs'. The curry is central to the event since within the recipe lies a grand narrative: several love stories, the conjoined sciences of the limited palettes of spice and colour, the space between languages and, of course, the love of food. It is a gastronomic *Gesamtkunstwerk* (universal artwork). To that end I have woven the recipe in and out of the following story, which is the one of how I came to cook the Fiction House Curry. It's a tale of the British Empire and the effect its great grinding wheels have had on just about every life that it reigned over. If you were to ask how I, a white Scotsman, dare to lay claim to a curry recipe, then please read on! My paintings and my cooking cross-fertilize each other as the years go on. A limited palette of spice and colours burst into something freer when I eventually made it to India myself.

ORIGINS

I am a Glasgow street kid wandering in and out of the derelict tenements my ancestors once lived in. Childhood food was tinned and smelled mostly of boiled vegetables. We didn't go on foreign holidays that might have offered a change of palate, so summer was spent playing in disused buildings ahead of demolition crews or in Kelvingrove Park between a nose-less statue of the philosopher Thomas Carlyle and a Boer War soldier. The latter, an anonymous pith-helmeted stone infantryman, wore puttees like Grandpa Pat, whose own lungs were petrified by German mustard gas in the Somme. Pat's slow death in 1941 prompted his son James, my uncle, to work off his grief as a stoker in the British Navy shovelling coal all the way to Karachi. I should add that King George V sent Pat a letter thanking him for his services to the Empire, and King George's statue was still standing at India Gate in Bombay when I got there in 1992.

The Glasgow streets that housed Pat, James, the foundry-workers and locomotive- and shipbuilders who built the hardware for King George's Empire were eventually deemed no longer fit for purpose and pulled down, decanting people like wine from the city to new suburbs. With no buildings to play in, I wandered on and wander still (it's a conflict since I am a painter of large pictures, and large pictures like to stay in one place). Only red gravel chips remained where the network of streets used to be. Not so the great buildings of Kelvingrove Art Gallery and Museum, built in 1901 for the Glasgow International Exhibition, where I first saw art, and the Kelvin Hall opposite, an exhibition arena built in 1927 by Thomas Gilchrist Gilmour and Thomas P. M. Somers. This pair, along with Glasgow University Tower, still dominate the landscape that I cycle through of a morning taking my kids to school. They carved a new nose for Carlye but smashed the face off the Boer War soldier. Nothing lasts for long. I made my paintings my permanent architecture. Ruptured territories held together in a holding structure of heterogeneity. The paintings are my fictional home, my Fiction House.

The long hot summer of 1976 found me in Kelvingrove Park most days, scoping out the world from halfway up a tree. Pakistani immigrants began to appear in larger numbers in the early years of that decade, and the cooking smells on Park Road, where many first settled, wrestled my nostrils into an olfactory lock-hold that didn't release me until after I was beyond the park gates. I wondered what went on inside these homes that generated such smells. Turning on the television before 9 a.m. on a Sunday gave me an idea. The half-hour BBC magazine programme 'Nai Zindagi Naya Jeevan' ('New Way New Life') presented news, current affairs and a music slot in Hindi and Urdu for a breakfast audience of South Asian immigrants. Superstars from the Subcontinent like Lata Mangeshkar and Ghulam Ali performed live and, although I did not belong to the target demographic, at 8 years old I too was recently arrived, and sat there transfixed, drinking them in with my cornflakes.

Acquiring milk for the aforementioned meal was the first way I came into contact with Asians in Glasgow. Their convenience stores, previously called dairies, were now referred to with casual racism. Our local Asian grocer had adopted the name Sam to avoid sounding too foreign just as in the 1930s my grandfather had changed his workplace name from Patrick to Peter to sidestep the systemic anti-Catholic bigotry of the Protestant worksite foremen in order to get a day's work. He had not been paid proper wages as a labourer building Great Western Rd, just dole money from the bureau of employment (called 'burroo' or 'brew' in Glaswegian dialect). He was a burroo navvy, an unemployed Irish immigrant from Donegal. He suffered bigotry but not racism. He was white, like me. A Gora, to use the parlance of the northern Subcontinent.

I was cautious and respectful with Asians, perhaps because of my Uncle James's tale of having been set upon by angry Hindus during the Second World War when he was stationed in Karachi – a revenge attack after a British Jeep had accidentally run over a sacred cow. James had had nothing to do with the Jeep incident but he was wearing the uniform and left for dead in a ditch. The long delicate fingers that covered his head to protect him from the blows were nicotine-stained by pipe-smoking, and cigarettes from age 9. He waved them in the air conducting his Chopin records and recounted how a school-teacher, cane in hand, had admitted their beauty and the pity of thrashing them, as they were the hands of a pianist.

Forty years later, when I was studying at Glasgow School of Art, a fellow student (who later won a Turner Prize) declared, 'There is finally a beautiful girl in the school!' She, a jeweller and I, a painter, strolled in that same Kelvingrove Park of childhood and, after lengthy entreaties, lay in secret under the same trees I had climbed. We kissed, she sweated and her sweat smelled of fenugreek. Her tummy rumbled and I mistook this for passion when it was in fact hunger. She would not eat until she returned home to the East End. We needed a room to take matters erotic and culinary further, since she was starving herself for fear of eating corrupted victuals outside the family home. I rented a room overlooking the River Kelvin and finally there was privacy for passion and a kitchen to cook in. Having started off as inexperienced at both, this little cell became a laboratory of desire. She taught me that onions are the base, but the first spice is cumin.

Opposite: *Breakers*, 2012.
Oil on canvas, 220 × 180 cm
(86 ⅝ × 70 ⅞ inches);
Right: *Uptan*, 2013.
Oil on canvas, 200 × 180 cm
(78¾ × 70 ⅞ inches).

Opposite: *Red Romans*, 2013.
Oil on canvas, 200 × 180 cm
(78 ¾ × 70 ⅞ inches).
Right: *Yellow Russians*, 1997.
Oil on canvas, 200 × 180 cm
(78 ¾ × 70 ⅞ inches).

Green Afghani, 2005. Oil on canvas,
220 × 180 cm (86 ⅝ × 70 ⅞ inches).

Wazir Khan, 2019. Oil on canvas,
220 × 180 cm (86 ⅝ × 70 ⅞ inches).

THE RECIPE

CUMIN (*ZEERA*)

There's a sensual aspect to this spice in my memory. After love came food. The word 'cumin' heralds the climax and thus with the end of passion comes the time for cooking. At 19 I still didn't know how to cook, so she taught me and I learned to cook Indian before anything else. Cumin is the start of so many things. Ground or whole seeds. The seeds that women pick through for chaff as through hair for lice. She stroked my hair pretending to chase down creepy crawlies and then did the same to the cumin seeds. The smell is wonderful but it's only the start; there is a saying that if there is too little to eat it is like a cumin seed in a camel's mouth

Slice 3–4 medium onions, some thin, some chunky.

Pour a good amount of oil into a pan over a medium heat and when it is hot add a soup spoon of the cleaned cumin seeds. They should pop when the oil is hot and release a wonderful smell. Onions next: brown them a bit, turn down the heat, cover and leave to cook for 20 minutes at least. Add salt after 10 minutes or so.

CHILLI (*MIRCH*)

Finely chop 3–4 chillies and add them to the softened onions. How many chillies to use depends on your taste and the strength of the chillies. The jeweller would run her finger over the knife after the first cut and touch her tongue to test the heat.

Green or red, lay them on your chopping board like complementary colours from a Fauvist painting. Use the skinny little long chillies. Cut off the point and the stem then slice them twice lengthwise to create four lengths, then chop into small pieces. I once mentioned to her an article I read that claimed too much chilli caused brain damage. She slapped

me across the face for this remark. The exact colour of green chilli is a mix of Prussian blue mixed with pure cadmium lemon. This is the green of my 1997 painting *Green Russians*. I saw those young Soviet recruits in Dresden walking to the station in their army uniforms in 1991, heading back to the remains of the USSR, another fallen empire.

If you prefer a darker sauce, then use red chillies but with fresh coriander (cilantro) sprinkled over. Chilli powder or dried chillies can also work.

GARAM MASALA (WARMING SPICES)

This spice blend is the equivalent to the earth colours, the umbers, ochres and siennas. The spice equivalents are cinnamon, cloves, black pepper, coriander and cumin. You don't need all of them but you need at least three. You can warm the spices in a hot pan until they start to give off some nice perfume, then grind them in a spice grinder while still warm. No spice grinder? Then put them in a bag and use a rolling pin to crush them down. Powdered spice is also fine, but not as pungent. The Dutch painter Frans Hals used an earth palette in his later works, and I tried to do the same when painting portraits of the jeweller. I found endless permutations of the earth palette on her face using ochres, and turquoise for the highlights, never white.

In the summer of 1989, a janitor who was unhappily married to a friend of my mother's made a copy of the side door entrance key to the great Mackintosh Building of The Glasgow School of Art. Mackintosh's masterpiece became our playground and lovers' palace. No fear of holding hands in public, no racist barbs. The Berlin Wall fell that winter. I painted many portraits of her there but none survived except as grainy Ektachrome slides. Then again, neither did the Mackintosh.

Add your garam masala and fry it a bit. Now add cold water to stop the cooking, then bring it to the boil again and evaporate it back down. This process is called 'pooning'. Do it three times.

TURMERIC (*HALDI*)

Turmeric was rubbed into the skin of a bridegroom in Karachi, as documented in my painting *Uptan*. It actually first surfaced in the *Yellow Russians* which used Indian yellow made from the urine of cows fed on mango leaves, as well as five other yellows. The colour of spice. India gave me both a recipe for cooking and one for painting. Both palettes/palates at the same time. Turmeric is added later in my recipe. I also add it to rice for colour – the poor person's saffron.

How much turmeric to use is a good question. Nowadays there is a health craze around it. I add a couple of heaped teaspoons to the sauce but also use it directly on the meat.

CORIANDER (*DHANIYA*)

This seed and leaf represents a principality in the kingdom of spice. Karachi pointed me in the direction of Park Road, to the grocers who sold food to the Asian community. In their shop, fresh coriander (cilantro) was heaped in great grassy knolls alongside vegetables whose names I still don't know. I learned to chop it up and add it to yogurt to make raita. Add it to an omelette with red chilli and cumin for a spicy breakfast. *Crushed coriander seed gives an extra citrus note to the curry.*

CARDAMOM (*ELAICHI*)

Cardamom was not love at first bite for me. I had it in my coffee in Aleppo and did not take kindly to it. It was only later, popping pods and discovering black cardamom (*badi elaichi*) that I inducted it into my store cupboard (pantry). This one

I added later. *Take a handful of green pods, crack them open and sprinkle into the mixture. Add in three black pods. The black pods are a rustic bass note whereas the green dance on the top of the tongue.*

FENUGREEK (*METHI*)
She sweated this out as we snogged in Kelvingrove Park and her tummy rumbled for fear of eating corrupted victuals outside the family home. I don't use fenugreek because of the sweat smell, but for some it is indispensable.

GINGER (*ADRAK*)
AND GARLIC (*LASUN*)
In Glasgow, 'ginger' is a sweet fizzy drink. As little kids we would rake through rubbish bins in tenement back courts for empty ginger bottles for which a deposit could be redeemed. We then bought sweets and munched them as we sat on the concrete bin shelter roof. Thus the word ginger needed to be re-conceptualized as a solid root rather than a sweet fizzy liquid. *You can buy garlic and ginger paste in a jar, but it is usually very salty. I often blitz the two together to reduce cooking time, but patient chopping of them both to tiny pieces is of course the higher path. Use too much rather than too little.* My current downstairs neighbour, who's from Punjab, leaves great chunks of ginger in her dishes, so find your own way.

THE CHICKEN
The one I use is from a grocery called KRK at the end of Park Rd. The guys know me there. I have to sing either 'Kabhi Kabhi' or 'Ye Kahani Phir Sahi' before they serve me. It's also the spot where I can practise my Urdu, which is evaporating as the years roll on. Some old-timers remember me from 30 years ago when I was walking out with my jeweller. There was always tension back then. Now we can

laugh, sometimes. I buy the whole chicken, neck and all, ready cut. *You can add this to the spice, but I like to sprinkle the meat with salt and powdered spices and roast it for half an hour in the oven then add it to the sauce.*

FINISHING THE DISH:
Adding details is quite subjective. At this point you should have a rich brown sauce that can be pushed in different directions. *Add the juice of fresh lime and some freshly chopped coriander.*

Alternatively, additions might be one or all of the following:

*chopped tomatoes (a can or
   3 fresh, chopped)
a good tablespoon of plain yogurt
   – best to let the dish cool a bit
   before adding to avoid curdling
a blob of lime pickle
some well fried onions
roasted red peppers
toasted flaked (slivered) almonds*

The dish ends and so does the story. Four years later the magnificent coloured enamelled necklace the jeweller made was bought by Kelvingrove Art Gallery and Museum. She moved on to the Royal College of Art in London and eventually married a designer. I kept moving. I worked at painting, cooking and singing in Prague where I thought my new life would start; shivering the winter away in the Holešovice district. For every song a painting. For every colour, a spice. My first guests were Americans who didn't know curry. My access to spice was limited. It was a limited palette that required mastery of a few fundamental flavours, more like a goulash … At the YMCA in Lahore I hung out with a bunch of decadent bachelor losers living in dirty rooms off an even filthier corridor. They had me supply them with booze, and ordered in karahi chicken, which we ate cross-legged on the floor around one

huge scalding metal platter. They helped me compose love letters in Urdu and taught me to sing 'Abhi to mein Javan Huun' ('While I am Still Young'). It was the song that was supposed to win back the jeweller.

Over the border in Amritsar I met a tabla player whose impromptu jam session/supper in the precinct of the Golden Temple was like the first Fiction House event. His old father sat in a snorkel jacket bent over a primus stove cooking *chana masala* (spiced chickpeas) while his best friend taught me the song 'Ye Kahani Phir Sahi' (will tell you more about this story/situation, some other time) made famous by Ghulam Ali. They all completed my education in one sense. In another I completed it myself in the courtyard of the Wazir Khan Mosque, which Jorge Luis Borges wrote about (without ever having visited it, of course) in the short story 'Blue Tigers'. I drew there every day for a week and chatted to Sufis and crazed street urchins who were mashed on ganja, singing for God until their hearts near burst out of their rib cages. The ablutions fountain is a symposium table gushing with blood-red wine and the song of exclamation as I touch a heart, not of darkness but of a deep other, a point of joy, of pure ecstasy pouring out like a great belch of satisfaction. Vulgar, affirmative, wordless yet truthful. It is the great 'Yes, yes, yes'.

Below: *3 Men Y.M.C.A Lahore*, 2019.
Oil on canvas, 200 × 180 cm
(78 ¾ × 70 ⅞ inches).

BREAD AND BUTTER PUDDING WITH PAWPAW CUSTARD AND PALM WINE GLAZE

INGREDIENTS

Nigerian Bread
Butter
Lime Marmalade
Evaporated Milk
Fresh Pawpaw
Brown Sugar
Eggs
Palm Wine

METHOD

Go to the bakery and buy a loaf of the sweet bread that is so beloved by Nigerians. We may like our meat tough but our bread is sweet and soft as brioche. My favorite bakeries in Port Harcourt are Skippers and Buraka.

Once you are home, slice the bread and cut the slices into diagonal halves to make triangles. Butter both sides of the triangles generously and spread lime marmalade onto one side. Lime marmalade is surprisingly hard to find. I order it off the Internet. You could always make your own, of course. It was my father's favorite preserve. When in England he would eat it on slices of white, medium-sliced, English bread that had first been slicked with soft margarine. It was the 1980s and margarine was deemed the healthy choice. I can see his fingers handle the bread delicately as he spreads the green marmalade on. He would chew loudly. Mouth closed, of course, but the noise was still audible. When I was younger I found the act of eating sad and solemn. Tragically human. Watching or hearing him eat made me think of him as vulnerable and in need of protection. My responsibility.

The bread and butter came at the end of his usual breakfast when he was in England: cornflakes with warm milk, followed by smoked mackerel with a wedge of lemon, then came the bread and marmalade washed down with black tea and lemon. It was my job to make his breakfast when he came to the house. I once met an Ogoni woman in New York, a refugee, who told me she used to feed him too when he was in detention in 1995. One day, the morning of the 10th of November, she visited the prison with her usual package of food. She was told to go home because 'he would not be needing food today'.

This dessert is about him. The committed Nigerian who never-
theless chose England for our childhood. Bread and butter
pudding. Marmalade. Boarding schools and custard. Pawpaw and
lime are his favorite Nigerian fruit. I am the girl in the
doorway of the kitchen watching the back of his head, listening
to him eating. His jaw working powerfully. He knows I am there
but does not turn around. Nor does he send me away.

Butter a deep baking tray and lay in the bread with the pointy
sides facing upwards. Then start the custard. Into a blender,
pour a large tin of Peak evaporated milk (the most popular brand
of evaporated milk in Nigeria), ripe chunks of pawpaw, sugar and
eggs. You can put in the whole egg, but for extra creaminess add
one or two extra yolks. Blend until perfectly smooth. No chunks
of pawpaw should remain. Pour the smooth, creamy pawpaw mixture
over the bread. Let it sit for 20 minutes so that the bread has
the chance to truly soak up the custard. Bake in a 350°F (175°C)
oven until just set, but not too hard.

While the pudding is in the oven, you can make a palm wine syrup
to glaze the dessert. Pour a fairly sweet palm wine into a clean
frying pan. It should not be more than 1 cm (½ inch) high. Add a
small piece of butter and 1 heaped tablespoon of sugar. Put it on
a medium heat and allow it to reduce. It will take some time. But
when it does, the resulting syrup is sparse, a little sharp, but
utterly ambrosial. Pour over the bread pudding and serve.

Kuchiko (Dried Sea Cucumber Ovaries)

In Japan, we eat sea cucumber. I have always respected the courage of the first person who tried eating sea cucumber and his or her imagination in thinking it might be edible. But more than this, *kuchiko* is a food made entirely of the ovaries of sea cucumbers. This is very special food even in Japan. It is not home-cooking at all. It is produced by some professional people in the Noto Peninsula that is not very far from Kanazawa on the island of Honshu.

I often think food is edible sculpture. When I look at this abstract art-looking *kuchiko*, I feel this most. Simply harvesting the ovaries is a task that requires a great deal of time and labour. Sometimes, more than a hundred sea cucumbers are needed to make one small triangle of orange *kuchiko*. I wanted to make this edible sculpture by myself. I went to Noto to learn how to make it.

Shimabuku

Preparation for the Installation at 21st Century Museum of Contemporary Art, Kanazawa 2013, shown opposite.

STEAMED EGG (Chinese)

STEAMED EGG

These recipes are written to mirror each other. One represents day, and the other night. Served in bowls and prepared by putting the ingredients through a sieve, both require a duration of time to rest and allow for the transformation from liquid to solid to take place. These dishes are transcultural, gluten-free, and adapted from family recipes.

Ingredients:

3 eggs
1 cup of chicken broth (stock)
    or you can substitute with vege-
    table broth, if you're vegetarian
2 teaspoons sesame oil
1 scallion (spring onion), finely
    chopped
steamed rice, to serve
tamari (gluten-free) or soy sauce
    (to taste), to serve

Serves 3–4

Instructions:

Thoroughly whisk the eggs in a bowl. Add the chicken broth (stock) to the eggs and gently whisk until fully incorporated.

Add 1 teaspoon of the sesame oil and whisk again gently to incorporate.

Pour the mixture through a fine-mesh sieve into a large heat-safe bowl for steaming.

Place the bowl in a steamer over medium heat and steam, covered, for 8 minutes until gently set.

Garnish with the scallion (spring onions) and sesame oil.

Serving instructions:

Serve with rice. Add a spoonful of tamari for added flavor.

"An infant plunging its hands into a jar of honey is instantly involved in contemplating the formal properties of solids and liquids and the essential relation between the subjective experiencing self and the experienced world. The viscous is a state half-way between solid and liquid. It is like a cross section in a process of change. It is unstable, but it does not flow. It is soft, yielding and compressible. Its stickiness is a trap, it clings like a leech; it attacks the boundary between myself and it."
                    – Jean-Paul Sartre
        "The phenomenon of stickiness"

PANNA COTTA WITH BERRY SAUCE (Italian)

PANNA COTTA

Ingredients:

6 tablespoons cold water
2 packets gelatin (about
  5 teaspoons)
2 cups heavy (double) cream
2 cups full-fat (whole) milk
⅓ cup white granulated sugar
2 teaspoons vanilla extract

Serves 6–8

Instructions:

Pour the cold water into a heatproof bowl. Sprinkle the gelatin over and mix, then let stand for 5–10 minutes until the gelatin is softened.

Heat the cream, milk, and sugar in a saucepan, stirring occasionally, over medium heat (keep it just below a simmer, do not let it boil).

Once the sugar is dissolved, remove the pan from the heat and stir in the vanilla extract.

Slowly pour the very warm panna cotta mixture over the gelatin in the bowl and stir until the gelatin is completely dissolved.

Pour the combined mixture through a fine-mesh sieve into a serving bowl.

Let the bowl of panna cotta chill in the refrigerator for at least 4 hours.

BERRY SAUCE

Ingredients:

24 oz raspberries
1 piece lemon rind, plus a squeeze
  of lemon juice (to taste)
1 cup water
¼ cup sugar, or to taste

Instructions:

Put the raspberries, lemon rind, and water into a pot over medium heat and bring to a simmer, mashing the berries as they cook to break them down.

Simmer for 5 minutes.

Pour the mixture through a sieve into a bowl to strain out the berry pulp (discard).

Pour the liquid back into the pot and bring back to a simmer to reduce by half, or until the sauce thickly coats the back of a spoon. Add the sugar and a small squeeze of lemon juice, then taste for sweetness.

Once done, let the sauce chill in the refrigerator.

Serving instructions:

Spoon the panna cotta into individual bowls then drizzle the berry sauce on top.

BORN 1954 : LIVES NEW YORK STATE, USA

Summer Salad with Shrimp

Serves 6–8

This salad came from enjoying the plants in the garden. It came to mind in the summer of 2020 during the pandemic because I made a large 'victory garden' and had bought food that was frozen, to make sure there would be something to eat.

The day before, buy a couple pounds of frozen shrimp (prawns) and thaw overnight. The next morning, prepare and marinate them, to be cooked that evening on the grill (barbecue).

If you don't have a grill the shrimp can easily be cooked under the broiler (grill).

IN THE MORNING:

First devein the thawed shrimp (prawns).

Soak 10 wooden skewers in water until time to grill.

In the garden or market, pick several sprigs of fresh oregano, thyme, a bunch of cilantro (coriander), as well as parsley, and any other savory herbs you like.

Also collect jalapeños, serrano peppers, or any chili peppers you like, depending on your heat preference.

For the marinade:

- herbs (see left)
- chili peppers, to taste (see left)
- 3 tablespoons olive oil
- juice of 1 lime (don't add too much lime juice as it will cook the shrimp)
- 6 cloves garlic
- 3 tablespoons of chopped fresh parsley
- zest of 1 lemon or lime
- 1 tablespoon or so of tomato paste (purée)
- 1 teaspoon salt
- ½ teaspoon pepper

Clean and roughly chop your herbs and chili peppers (discarding the seeds) and blend them in your blender with the olive oil, lime juice, garlic, parsley, lemon or lime zest, tomato paste (purée), salt, and pepper, then taste and adjust.

Toss your shrimp in a bowl with the marinade, cover and refrigerate until the evening.

IN THE EVENING:

Collect shiso leaves, basil, arugula (rocket), salad greens, and any other greens you like.

Wash and dry your greens. You will need enough to fill a large salad bowl.

For the salad dressing:

- 1 large shallot
- 1 tablespoon salted capers, rinsed
- 1 teaspoon Dijon mustard
- 4 tablespoons olive oil
- 2 tablespoons oak barrel-aged Champagne vinegar (or any vinegar you like; you can add garlic and more lime juice if you like)
- ¼ teaspoon salt

Finely chop the shallot and capers and mix in a bowl with the Dijon mustard, olive oil Champagne vinegar, and salt.

Rip the salad greens with your hand. Chiffonade the shiso leaves and basil. For that, I stack up the leaves and tightly roll them up and cut very finely with a sharp knife or kitchen scissors. Put them into a large bowl with the arugula (rocket) and salad greens.

Skewer your shrimp: Place the first skewer through the tail end of the marinated shrimp and then near the head so the shrimp looks like a spiral. For the next shrimp, place the skewer in the middle of the shrimp so that it drapes over the first shrimp. Continue in this pattern for 3–4 more shrimp. Repeat with the rest of the shrimp and skewers.

Heat up your grill (barbecue) or oven and grill the shrimp until they are no longer translucent. I like them a bit charred myself. They typically take 2–3 minutes per side.

Once your shrimp are cooked, dress the salad.

Plate the dressed salad with your skewered shrimp to the side. The salad does not keep but the shrimp are very good the next day.

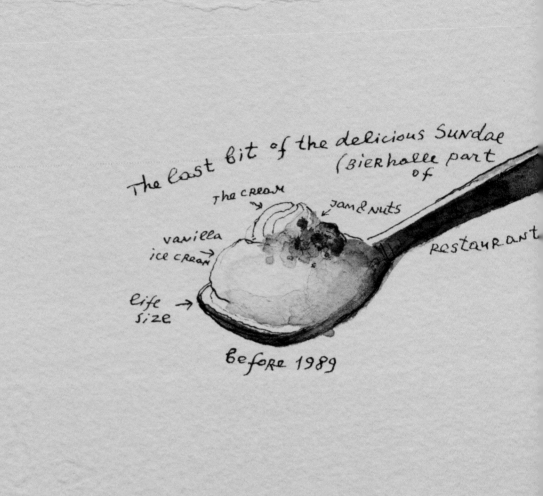

The last bit of the delicious Sundae
(Bierhalle part of

The Cream

Jam & nuts

vanilla
ice cream

RESTAURANT

life
size

before 1989

SOLAK Sund

LGARIA")

↓ still had some hair

after 1989 (1990)
← CREAM & pineapple (A LOT)

PROject

соллк'20
18.7.

<u>Solak Sundae</u>

I have always loved ice cream sundaes.

Back in my youth, during socialism in my native Bulgaria, it was pretty rare to have a real sundae – I mean besides the obvious vanilla ice cream, you also had to have the whipped cream, the syrup, the jam, the nuts, and so on. There was this famous Bulgarian restaurant in Sofia, and in its basement, there was a place strangely enough called a 'Bierhalle' even though, as I discovered much later when I started travelling in Europe, it didn't look at all like a typical German Bierhalle; anyway, our family usually dined there whenever we had to spend a day in Sofia coming from my home town of Gabrovo (Christo was born there, by the way). And I had always the same meal: beef soup, baked veal, and as a dessert – their Sundae, the most delicious dessert I could imagine. In general, there was no cream in Bulgaria at that time. I really don't know why, but there was no cream. And in that restaurant they used to prepare their own cream and a rather modest dollop of such cream was placed on top of the ice cream, along with strawberry or raspberry jam and a tiny load of ground walnuts. What a pleasure it was to slowly eat that most delicious thing and to leave for the very last bite the final bit of ice cream, carefully arranged on the special spoon, with almost all of the whipped cream which I deliberately didn't touch (it always seemed like such a small amount), some of the jam and all of the ground nuts. I can still feel that heavenly experience in my mouth.

Years later when democracy came and there was no shortage of anything (except money), one day I decided to enjoy in full, with no boundaries, that whipped cream that was so missing during socialism. So, under the rather suspicious gaze of my wife (who is an amazing cook, by the way), I took a big glass bowl, emptied around half a kilo of canned pineapple (that fruit was also missing during my youth) and sprayed on top of it the full contents of a big can of whipped cream. I sat down and started eating that (enormous) pleasure. Needless to say, I got sick and I am not sure that I finished up the pleasure at all.

Now I am over sixty, much more settled down, but still loving desserts – in a more moderate way, of course. I am a strange person, in general. For example, I stopped drinking alcohol in early 1982 (there were serious concerns that my 20-year-old baby sister might have breast cancer and I swore that if the check-up was okay I would stop drinking alcohol), and since then I have never ever put a drop of alcohol in my mouth. Except if that drop is to flavour a sundae, then my conscience accepts it and I eat it.

p. 230–231: *Solak Sundae*, 2020. Sepia, black and white ink, and wash on paper, 19 × 28 cm (7½ × 11 inches)

Enough with the introduction, here is my own Solak Sundae recipe (with a little help from my wife and daughter, who, like her mother, is an outstanding cook):

Ingredients:

- a small handful (about 70 grams) of fresh blueberries;
- a dozen fresh raspberries;
- four scoops of vanilla ice cream;
- one teaspoon of wild strawberry jam, blueberry jam
  and white cherry jam (the latter should be homemade
  with geranium);
- two tablespoons of chokeberry syrup;
- 150 grams of real dairy cream, 31% fat, whipped with
  80 grams of powdered sugar;
- one tablespoon of coarsely ground toasted walnuts;
- colourful round sprinkles for decoration.

Take a melba dish, not so large (for obvious reasons). Put the fresh fruit in the bottom, but leave aside three raspberries and one blueberry. Put the four scoops of ice cream on top of the fruit, and then put one spoonful of each of the three jams on them. Drizzle two tablespoons of chokeberry syrup on top. Pipe on the whipped cream, scatter on the walnuts and part of the sprinkles, and on the very top arrange the three raspberries with the blueberry in the middle, and one brightly coloured sprinkle in the blueberry's calyx.

And start eating, as it will melt.

And don't forget to have at hand a glass of cold, almost ice-cold, water, to drink after the last sweet bite, but not immediately; no, one has to wait some seconds, until your mouth really starts begging for cold water; then to emphasize even further that thirsty feeling you can imagine that actually you don't have a glass of ice-cold water next to your left hand, and then, only then, you can pick up the glass and drink it. Only when one kills the sweet Solak Sundae taste can the sublimity of that sweetness be experienced. The glass has to have a thin edge, a thick edge doesn't work if you want to really enjoy the cold water. The meaning of daily life also consists of such tiny little requirements but fulfilled to the max.

Nedko Solakov, with the help of Slava Nakovska, my devoted wife. Translated and edited by Angela Rodel.

Deconstructed Arancini
for Sixteen-month-old Twins

<u>Serves</u> 1 pair of sixteen-month-old twins

2 x arancini balls (filling: ragù)
1 x set of sixteen-month-old twins

Take one set of sixteen-month-old twins.

Remove their clothes, but keep on their diapers.

When they are prepared, place the set of twins into two high chairs.

Next, remove both arancini balls from the paper bag.

Break each arancini ball into halves and place on the twins' high chair trays.

Separate the ragù filling from the arancini rice.

Do not provide cutlery or crockery.

Place a substantial protective covering over your clothes and head.

Watch as the set of sixteen-month-old twins throw the ragù filling.

Wait as the set of twins eat the arancini rice, grain by grain.

When the ragù has entirely left the tray, and is either on the floor, the walls, the twins' feet, chest, hands, arms, perhaps in their mouths, certainly in their hair, or (less likely) in their stomachs, and when they seem to have lost interest in the rice, remove one twin from the high chair, place at ground level, urge twin to not move, try to catch him as he moves, then remove the other twin. Urge her not move. Catch her as she moves.

Hastily pick up the set of sixteen-month-old twins and put them into a running shower.

Run water at tepid heat and rinse the set of sixteen-month-old twins until the water runs clear, instead of with ragù.

S pecially
P rocessed
A merican
M e

Photo credit Mari Uchida

"

스팸먹을때는 전쟁생각도 나지. 미국사람들이 거기서 나눠줬어. 처음 먹을때 그냥, 뚜껑 여니까 그냥 막 먹었지. 너무 맛있었지. 지금 먹으니까 맛이없다, 하하. 응, 먹을게 많아서.

When I eat SPAM it reminds me of the war. The Americans shared it with us. The first time I ate it, I opened the lid and scarfed it down. It was so delicious. When I eat it now, it doesn't taste good, haha. Mmm, because there's plenty to eat.

"

– 인정렬 Chong Yol In, my grandma

Specially Processed American Me.
That's the title of my autobiographical performance: a backronym for SPAM with "Me" in place of "Meat." In many ways, being Asian American has a lot in common with SPAM. We're marginalized, misunderstood, born in America yet questioned by white Americans, and shaped by war.

I'm Korean American and like many Asian American families from US military-occupied war-torn lands— Korea, Japan, the Philippines, Hawaii, Guam—my family always had SPAM on hand. Now SPAM's just as much Asian as it is American. It's used in Budae Jjigae, Chanpurū, Silog, Musubi, Kelaguen. It's fusion without the snobbery. Fusion for survival. Fusion because it's delicious.

SPAM sales skyrocketed during the pandemic, which makes sense since it's a shelf-stable emergency food. But I think there's more to it than that. I bet a lot of Asian Americans like me bought extra cans for comfort. Despite its violent origins, SPAM reminds us of home because we never ate it anywhere else. It awakens memories: my mom packing my school lunch—SPAM fried rice and egg with a ketchup smile. I smile back.

– Jaime Sunwoo, me

SPAM FRIED RICE

스 팸 볶 음 밥

Photo credit Zach Bell

```
PIG      You are what you eat.
JAIME    Fried rice?
PIG      더 자세히 봐.
JAIME    Peas? Carrots?
PIG      Get to the meat of the matter.
JAIME    ...SPAM?
```

— An excerpt from my play

Serves 4. Cooking Time: 30 minutes

2 eggs, beaten
2 cloves garlic, minced
6 oz SPAM (½ can), diced
8 oz frozen mixed vegetables
3 cups cooked white rice
¼ tsp black pepper
2 tbsp soy sauce
1 tsp sesame oil
1 tsp toasted sesame seeds
2 scallion (spring onion) stalks, minced
2 tbsp of your preferred cooking oil
Sriracha and/or ketchup, to taste

Heat 1 tbsp of cooking oil in a large pan over medium heat. Add garlic and SPAM. Cook until crispy. Add mixed vegetables (i.e. corn, peas, carrots—whatever you like!). Cook until tender. Add rice and evenly distribute throughout. Add soy sauce, sesame oil, black pepper, and sesame seeds. Stir until even. Heat 1 tbsp of cooking oil in a small pan over low heat. Add eggs and cook both sides. Serve the SPAM fried rice in a bowl and top with the egg folded over. Garnish with scallion (spring onion). Finally, draw a smiley face on the egg with some Sriracha or ketchup.

— Recipe from my grandma to my mom to me to you

Learn more about the project and share your thoughts on SPAM at speciallyprocessed.com

SPECIALLY PROCESSED AMERICAN ME

BORN 1961 : LIVES NEW YORK, USA; BERLIN, GERMANY; AND CHIANGMAI, THAILAND

THAI CURRY PIZZA

Makes 4 x 10-inch pizzas

For the bases and sauce

4 x 9-oz pieces ready-made pizza dough
1 x 4-oz can green or red curry paste
1 tablespoon vegetable oil
2 tablespoons granulated or grated palm sugar,
 plus extra to taste
2 tablespoons fish sauce, plus extra to taste
1 x 14-fl oz can coconut milk
all-purpose (plain) flour or cornmeal, for dusting

For the green curry pizza toppings

2 tablespoons butter, for greasing
14–16 oz Wagyu beef steak (about 1 inch/
 2.5 cm thick)
1 eggplant (aubergine), very thinly sliced
 (about 1/32 inch/1–2 mm thick)
6 oz mozzarella cheese, torn into pieces
flaky sea salt
Parmesan cheese, grated, to serve
Thai basil leaves, to serve

For the red curry pizza toppings

1 lb duck breasts
8 oz oyster mushrooms
6 oz mozzarella cheese, torn into pieces
flaky sea salt
Thai basil leaves, to serve

You will also need

cast-iron skillet or frying pan
2 saucepans
digital probe thermometer
pizza stone

1.
Go to your local pizza place and buy 4 pieces of pizza dough. Keep in the fridge until the sauce and rest of the ingredients are ready.

2.
Prepare the sauce. Heat the red or green curry paste and the vegetable oil in a saucepan over low heat for 5–8 minutes. Add the palm sugar and fish sauce, stirring until the sugar dissolves. If it's too dry, add half a can of coconut milk. Once the sugar has dissolved, add the rest of the coconut milk, bring to the boil and reduce the heat. Don't over boil it. Taste and add sugar or fish sauce if needed. (Palm sugar helps bring down the heat.)

3.
Prepare and cook the Wagyu beef, or the duck breast and oyster mushrooms:

For the Wagyu beef
Heat your cast-iron skillet or frying pan over high heat. Grease the skillet lightly with butter. For a rare finish, sear the beef for 3 minutes per side, seasoning it with flaky sea salt. Remove the beef from the pan and let it rest before cutting into thin slices to top the green curry pizza.

For the duck breast
Using the tip of a sharp knife, score the skin of the duck and salt it with flaky sea salt. Place the duck breast skin-side down in the cast-iron skillet on medium-low heat and cook for about 5 minutes. Check the skin—it should be crispy and golden. Pour away any excess fat in the pan. Continue to cook the duck until the internal temperature reads 125°F (50°C) when tested using a digital probe thermometer. Flip the breast to the flesh side and cook until the temperature reads 140°F (60°C). Remove it from the pan and let it rest before cutting into thin slices.

For the oyster mushrooms
Heat the duck fat left behind in the skillet over medium heat. Spread the mushrooms out in a single layer in the pan. Cook, undisturbed, for 3–5 minutes until they start to brown. Stir them and cook for 3–5 minutes more until browned all over. Remove them from the pan and set aside.

4.
Take the 4 pieces of pizza dough out of the refrigerator and leave at room temperature for 10–15 minutes.

5.
Put the pizza stone into the oven and preheat to 425°F (220°C).

6.
Roll out the 4 pieces of pizza dough on the work counter, dusting with flour or cornmeal as needed to prevent it from sticking.

7.
Spoon 2–4 tablespoons of either red or green curry sauce onto the top of each pizza base. Top the green curry sauce with the sliced eggplant (aubergine) and 2–4 tablespoons of mozzarella; top the red curry sauce with oyster mushrooms and 2–4 tablespoons of mozzarella.

8.
Place each pizza on the hot pizza stone and cook for 12–15 minutes, depending on your oven.

9.
When ready, top the green curry pizza with thin slices of Wagyu beef, Parmesan cheese, and Thai basil, and the red curry pizza with thin slices of duck breast and Thai basil. If needed, spoon more sauce on top of the meat. Store any leftover sauce in the refrigerator for another use.

Wagyu beef; duck breasts; frying the duck breasts

Pizza dough; green curry paste; eggplant (aubergine)

Thai green curry pizza with Wagyu beef, eggplant (aubergine), mozzarella, Parmesan cheese, and Thai basil

Thai red curry pizza with oyster mushrooms, duck breast, mozzarella, and Thai basil

PART 1

YOUR PLEASURE UNDERSTANDS MINE

I. THE DINNER IS A PLAY

Start with the theme of your dinner. Think of your dinner as a theatre play. Imagine the entire room and your guests. Give a title to your dinner. This will be the guiding principle for your ideas. Make sure your concept will make your guests' tongues think. Food is the glue for the experience that you are about to host.

II. THE PLAY IS DIVIDED INTO CHAPTERS

Amber Ice (Another Map to Nevada, commissioned by The Performance Agency, Berlin, July 2020), see page 251 for the recipe.

Use the format of a multi-course dinner and flip it. Every course becomes a chapter, a moment to introduce a new part of your dinner-play. Your story is told through food, through dishes and their display. Introduce different tastes in a thoughtful order and create weird-looking edible moments.

Introduce to your guests to a selection of ingredients and recipes that have a connection to the story you would like to share.

Analyze the meaning of the special dishes you would like to add, research their history, place of origins and how they may have changed our world.

What does it mean to serve pineapple? And sugar cane? And oysters?

Give a name to each moment and decide how that moment plays a role within the full dinner-play.

Sounds can help you to tell your story, create a mood or enhance the palates of your guests. Choose the soundtrack, DJ or a harpist to design the atmosphere. Or let the cooking sounds and guests' stomachs do the trick.

Use music to announce each new chapter, as an introduction to a new dish.

The waiters are there to help you to create your play; they are actors in your dinner-play.

Are they going to dance in flavours? Are they writers who are reciting your menu as a poem?

Think of the given space as somewhere to dine in a very new format. We are not necessarily dining in a traditional way. The rules of the play are yours. Think of the space as a way to digest the story.

IV. THE TABLE IS THE STAGE

Natureza-Morta Nr. 1-2020

Food is nature, and it is our deepest and most direct connection to it.

The table is the stage that is used to display nature fully.

Do not take for granted the potential to give food its deserved place – the table is a sacred place, a sanctuary. Use all the allegories, fabrics, colours, props and devices you have to hand.

Anything can be a plate. What are the vessels that will hold your meal?

V. FOOD AS SCULPTURE

Look at the shapes that nature brings to you. Put them on top of each other. Fragment a cornucopia. Freeze, dust, cure, colour, create steam and smoke. Even the most simple ingredient or dish is already a sculpture.

VI. FOOD AS PAINTING

Roses (Berlin Art Week, HuA
International, Sep. 2020)

Don't think of recipes. Paint with food instead. Use the colour scheme that you please. Flavours work as colours. Trust the colour compositions and you will create delightful moments.

VII. BREAD IS LOVE BETWEEN STRANGERS

Encourage people to eat together. Food is our common denominator, so get them to share guttural gestures together. As we taste particles of the planet, we create a sublime intimacy.
   Your pleasure understands mine.

PART 2

RECIPES AND IDEAS

I. ABACAXI-KEBAB

Abacaxi-Kebab (Tabula
Rasa, commissioned by
foodculturedays, Jenisch
Musée, Vevey, Switzerland,
Sep. 2019)

Abacaxi is the Tupi name for pineapple. It has its origins in what we know today as Brazil. For the original inhabitants of the Brazilian land, the *abacaxi* was given as a symbol of hospitality.

The Europeans fell in love with the crowned fruit and during the colonization period a pineapple would cost a lot of money, the price of a luxury car today. The aristocracy would rent them to decorate their parties. Today a pineapple can be found for two dollars at any supermarket in the world.

What you need:

DOMESTIC KEBAB MACHINE
PINEAPPLE
OLIVE OIL
SALT
CORIANDER SEEDS
BASIL
LIME
POMEGRANATE
TORTILLA OR ANY THIN CRISPY BREAD
CHILLI PASTE
A COLOURFUL LATIN OR ARABIC-STYLE TABLECLOTH

Go to a department store or a good online shop. Ask for a domestic kebab machine.

Choose a ripe and succulent pineapple. Cut its skin off.

Choose an interesting colourful tablecloth with a Latin or Arabic theme to display your kebab-pineapple creation.

Roast your pineapple for 1½ hours on your kebab machine, brushing the outside with a mixture of olive oil, salt and crushed coriander seeds to make it golden and crispy.

Blend a mix of basil with olive oil, salt and lime juice.

De-seed a pomegranate.

Get your crispy tortilla, spread some of your favourite chilli paste, chop some of your roast pineapple, a drizzle of your basil oil and a few jewels of pomegranate.

II. THE BLUE OYSTERS

When I was 6 or 7 years old I was watching *Police Academy* with my uncles on the couch. There was a scene in which the police enter a male gay bar called 'The Blue Oyster Bar'. In that scene, the policemen got scared when they saw the men being intimate and dancing with each other. The men in my family laughed. I felt strangely sad.

Blue Oysters (Tabula Rasa, commissioned by foodculturedays, Jenisch Musée, Vevey, Switzerland, Sep. 2019)

Oysters are animals that change sex during their lives. They are naturally trans. The blue butterfly pea flower tea dyes everything blue naturally.

The tea and the oysters are natural.

What you need:
White clay
Kiln
Blue butterfly pea flower tea
Pearl glaze oysters
Lemons
Large mirror

Get some white clay and in a rough way, using your hands, turn it into a large shell. Fire it in a kiln and glaze it with a bright pearly tone. This will be the vessel for your oyster bar.

Heat up 10 litres of water and infuse with the butterfly pea tea. You can balance how dark the blue colour is. Put the naturally dyed tea into large plastic bags and freeze them.

Shuck your oysters and serve with lemons and frozen tea on a mirror.

III. AMBER ICE (IN 5 LATITUDES)

What you need:
Fish, Chipotle, Potato, Pineapple and Pomegranate

Freeze them all.
Taste it.

IV. FAROFA EARTH

Farofa Earth
(commissioned by
foodculturedays,
Alimentarium, Vevey,
Switzerland, Nov. 2017)

What you need:
Butter, Onions, Garlic, Chilli flakes, Manioc flour, Cacao powder, Salt, to taste, Plant vase, Boiled root vegetables

In a large pan, heat some butter, add the finely chopped onions and fry them with the finely chopped garlic and the chilli flakes for a few minutes. Add the manioc flour and toast with this mixture. Add salt to taste.

Add enough cacao powder so that the mixture looks like soil.

Get your plant vase and add some boiled root vegetables of your choice, then cover them with your farofa earth. Throw the farofa earth on your guests' tables as a side dish.

BABUSHKA'S BORSCHT
(A VEGETARIAN CABBAGE-BASED BORSCHT)

* * *

Makes 5–5.5 litres

* 6 large potatoes, peeled
* 1½ beetroot (beets), 1 peeled and
  cut into quarters, ½ grated
* 3 litres water
* 200 g + 50 g butter
* 200 g single (light) cream or milk
* 1 large onion, chopped fine
* ½ green pepper, chopped fine
* small bunch celery leaves, chopped fine
* 1 carrot, grated
* 800 g chopped canned tomatoes
* 50 g very finely shredded cabbage
* a little chopped dill (to taste)
* ½–¾ cabbage, shredded
* salt and pepper
* chopped dill, sour cream
  and rye bread, to serve

Fill a 6-litre pot with water. Add the potatoes and beetroot (beet) quarters (for colouring) and season with salt. Bring the pot to the boil and cook until the potatoes are tender. Drain but don't throw away the water (return it to the pot and keep it over a gentle heat). Discard the beets, transfer the potatoes to a bowl and mash them with the 200 g of butter and the cream or milk.

Heat the 50 g butter in a large frying pan, then sauté the onion, green pepper, celery leaves, grated beetroot and grated carrot for 15 minutes until tender. Towards end of sautéing add the chopped tomatoes. Continue to sauté for 10 minutes. Add the very finely shredded cabbage and dill to the pan and sauté. Season with pepper and salt.

Add the mashed potatoes gradually to the pot of gently heating water, stirring between additions. Add the contents from the frying pan to the pot, stir, and gradually add the shredded cabbage. Simmer without bringing to a boil (otherwise the cream will curdle).

Serve the borscht with dill, sour cream and rye bread. This amount is enough for several meals. Soup freezes well.

This is my Russian grandmother's borscht recipe. I usually make it in the autumn (fall) when beetroots, carrots, and cabbage are harvested. When I am asked to participate in a cooking venture, I often make this soup; for example, in 1972 I made my first art city appearance as Mr. Peanut in New York. I had travelled from Vancouver with fellow artists Michael Morris, Glenn Lewis, J. J. Baylin and Gathie Falk. A highlight of the visit included being invited by Gordon Matta-Clark to help prepare the New York Corres Sponge Dance School of Vancouver feast at 'Food' Restaurant. The New York Corres Sponge Dance School of Vancouver, coined by artist Glenn Lewis, was a casual getting together of friends and colleagues. There was no membership. People met for swimming, feasting and all forms of artistic events and celebrations. For the feast I prepared borscht and covered the restaurant floor with peanuts. I continue making this soup and each time have a séance with my grandmother, who is long ago deceased. Whenever possible I pass this recipe on.

Vincent Trasov

Babyland Bath Mr. Peanut with Granada Gazelle 1974

The excellence of rare flavours always brings us joy. The presentation's originality enriches this exceptional moment from the first bite.

My aesthetic inclination is towards the elegance of black. Here, there are no artifices, no unnecessary distractions. There is only the essential.

This is why, coupled with the talented and celebrated Michelin-starred chef and my good friend, Chef Philippe Da Silva, I propose the following recipe for an original dish.

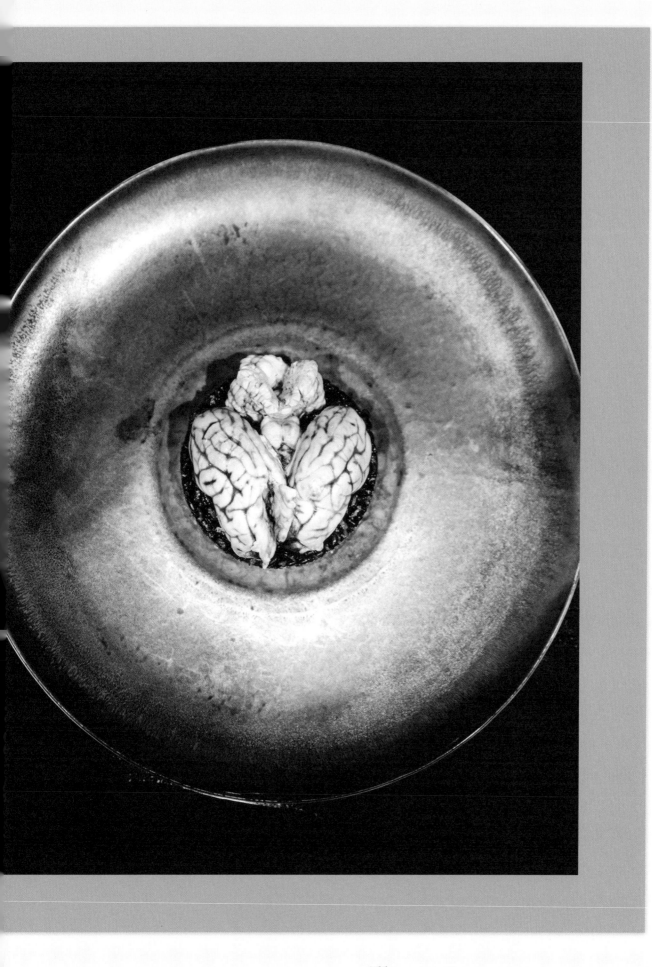

Lamb Brains and Venere Rice with Squid Ink Crêpes Dentelles

Serves 2

For the rice:
  100 g venere black rice
      (produced in the Po Valley in Italy)
  butter
  ½ onion, chopped
  100 g mushrooms, chopped
  1 tablespoon chopped parsley
  2 tablespoons small capers in vinegar
  salt

For the brains:
  2 lamb brains
  wine vinegar
  1 sprig thyme
  1 sprig bay leaves
  pinch of salt
  butter
  lemon juice

For the squid ink crêpes dentelles:
  25 g plain (all-purpose) flour
  40 g olive oil, plus extra for oiling
  200 g water
  ½ teaspoon squid ink

Rice preparation:
Cook the rice in a pan of salted water for 20 minutes until tender. Drain and reserve.

Melt some butter in a pan, add the chopped onion, mushrooms, parsley and small capers in vinegar. Season with salt and cook gently until the onion is soft. Mix into the rice.

Lamb brain preparation:
Bring a pan of water to a boil and add some wine vinegar, the sprigs of thyme and bay leaves and salt. Add the lamb brains and poach for 4 minutes. Drain and set aside.

Heat some butter in a sauté pan until frothy and sauté the brains with a squeeze of lemon juice.

Form the rice into two small round moulds, put them onto serving plates and set a brain atop each. Drizzle with the butter remaining in the pan.

Squid ink crêpe dentelle preparation:
Mix together half of the flour, olive oil, water and squid ink in a bowl. Add to a lightly oiled pan and cook for 4 minutes. This results in a very crisp crêpe dentelle, which should be balanced above a lamb brain. Repeat to make the second crêpe dentelle.

LAMB BRAINS AND VENERE RICE WITH SQUID INK CRÊPES DENTELLES

FIRE AND MEAT. A PLAN OF ACTION
by Volker Hobl

I have learned how to perfectly dry, mature, pickle, marinate and prepare different parts of meat, depending on their texture; by braising, steaming, frying and cooking sous-vide. I use stoves that work perfectly and allow for precise adjustment of heat. When Danh Vo asked me if we could organize a meal in Güldenhof, a remote former agricultural production co-operative a good hour from Berlin, the concept came to me quickly: a freshly slaughtered lamb, an open fire, vegetables. A total, almost archaic, back-to-basics approach. Improvised and experimental cooking. I wanted answers to a few questions:

What does freshly slaughtered meat taste like? (Normally the meat we prepare is several days, even weeks old.) What effect does the heat radiating from the fire have on the animal's body? What kind of wood is best and how much taste is added by the smoke? How do wind and weather affect the cooking? Which vegetables can be cooked – without any cookware – directly in the embers and which need to be cooked on a grill?

— **WEDNESDAY**
pho, grill-making, steel cross

Pho: A staple in Güldenhof that nowadays includes bones and beef. The stock (broth) is poured over soaked rice noodles and a crazy amount of very hot chillies, then spring onions (scallions), coriander (cilantro) and Thai basil are added. The pho is flavoured with a fish sauce made with the addition of lime, chilli and garlic (from the greenhouse).

The BBQ: We find a double-wire mesh fence at a steel merchant in the town of Neuruppin that we bend and turn into grills. We need them in different heights and sizes so that we can alter the cooking temperature for the different vegetables.

The cross for the lamb: For the lamb we weld a cross from 1.4-cm- (½-inch-) thick steel rods, like the Argentine gauchos use for asado, which is held up by a simple steel stand. It is built in such a way that you can rotate the cross from time to time – for us, every 30 minutes.

— **THURSDAY**
Pomeranian sheep,
Pyrenean Mountain Dog puppies

The meat: The shepherd, Reinhard, is Danh's neighbour. His flock mostly consists of Pomeranian Coarsewool sheep, Boer goats and a cross between Boer, forest and German Edelziege goats. He mainly uses the herd for countryside preservation: the goats take care of the bushes and the sheep take care of the grass. In the barn there are two adolescent lambs and the ram. We decide to cook only one of the lambs and select a black Pomeranian Coarsewool kid. To condemn an animal to death is always a difficult decision. As it should be.

Puppies like polar bears. There's also Zoe, a Pyrenean Mountain Dog, also known as a Patou, with her five puppies. The dogs are there to defend the sheep against the Brandenburg wolves; their barking goes right through you. Even the puppies, who are only a few days old, seem to be as big and strong as polar bear cubs.

— FRIDAY
harvesting vegetables, concrete explosions, newly slaughtered lamb

Vegetables: We buy leek, fennel and radish for the next few days from Lena and Philipp who work near a vegetable garden. Grilled radish is particularly nice and tastes excellent lukewarm with oil and lemon. The squash with the funny name Sweet Dumpling look like pale yellow peppers with dark green spots; they are the perfect size to be cooked directly in the embers, wrapped in a salt crust. We'll also prepare the celeriac (celery root) in the same way. We'll knead the dough for the salt crust today (two parts flour, one part fine salt, one part water).

Mass production: The first guests arrive in the evening. Reinhard brings the still-warm, slaughtered sheep. It weighs about 14 kg. The lungs and heart are immediately put in water and the black, dense fur is stretched and salted so that it can be sent for tanning later. It smells strongly of sheep ammonia and what you want andouillette to smell like. The naked, still-warm carcass smells of cream and hay. We tie it to the cross and then weld a second cross-brace for a perfect fit.

Baptism of fire: The test run for the fire pit doesn't go as expected. Small explosions fling embers several metres into the surrounding area. We assume that we have a problem with the wood. We're using beech and oak logs from trees in Güldenhof. In fact, the old concrete slabs the yard is made from are the problem. They can't withstand the high temperature, so we build a base from some bricks we find lying around.

— SATURDAY
a hefty hangover, wine on tap, giant kohlrabi, dancing around the fire

Slow food: As with all parties, the anticipation is always great, and ours is no exception. The fire carries on burning and the guests celebrate, drink and play cards into the early hours. It was a long time before anyone stirred this morning. Apart from me. Around 8 a.m. I light the fire again. I assume that the lamb needs to be on the fire for at least 6–8 hours. In the end, it takes 9 hours to cook. As I quickly note, the open fire and the constant breeze cook the lamb slowly.

Wine accompaniment: Jacob from Copenhagen arrives to install his wine and beer taps. A natural wine from the Provence winery Les Terres Promises, at the foothills of Sainte-Baume massif, flows freely. 'It's an easy-drinking and juicy wine without any chemicals added', says Jacob, and he's right. We hollow

out a kohlrabi of the giant variety – it is at least as large as a medicine ball – and we use it as a soup terrine. The kohlrabi pulp is the basis for the soup.

More vegetables: A dark-green Hokkaido pumpkin sits on the grill at the edge of the fire for several hours, cooking in its own juices. Once the seeds and the charred skin are removed, it is mashed and seasoned like potatoes. The leeks also roast on the fire. The outer layer burns, but the core is juicy and soft.

Piggiewagon: Meanwhile, my 8-year-old son Hugo and 10-year-old Vico are driving a pink, electric food van, affectionately named Piggiewagon, across the grounds, past the huge blocks of marble that Danh has erected. For both of them, this is their first time driving a real vehicle. They manage it mostly without accident.

No dry-ageing: We get the crockery from the main house with a cargo bike and we eat by the fire. For a 14-kg lamb, 9 hours of cooking time is extremely long, but the meat is succulent and exceptionally juicy. It is tender, as if it were cooked entirely sous-vide. The cultural technique of dry-ageing is clearly not required in order to tenderize the meat of freshly slaughtered sheep. Every last morsel of lamb is eaten and the bones are put straight into a pot to be made into stock later.

No sleep: Nguyen, Danh's brother, gets the music system from the house, extra fire pits are lit, the guests take off their jumpers, hoodies and T-shirts and dance topless between the fires. Aaron, Lena and Philipp's 16-month-old son, staggers as if light-headed between the dancers, too tired to keep his eyes open, yet too fascinated to not watch, let alone fall asleep.

A few days later in Berlin, Danh will serve lungs and heart in another pho.

One dish that I enjoy preparing is Thieboudienne, or "fish and rice," the national dish of Senegal. This recipe comes from my good friend, renowned Senegalese-American chef Pierre Thiam. It is borrowed from his cookbook, *Senegal: Modern Recipes from the Source to the Bowl.*

THIEBOUDIENNE

Serves 10

Ingredients:

1   large whole *thiof* (grouper) about 5 lb, cleaned and cut into about 7 steaks 1½ inches (4 cm) thick, reserving the head and tail
1   quantity *rof* (see recipe below right)
1   cup vegetable oil
1   white onion, chopped
1   green pepper, deseeded and chopped
2   cups tomato paste (purée)
5   cups water
½   green cabbage, cut into 3 wedges
1   cup *bisaap* (dried white hibiscus flowers)
2   Scotch bonnet peppers
2   palm-sized pieces *guedj* (dried, salted, and smoked fish, see Note, below)
2   pieces *yeet* (fermented sea snails), rinsed (see Note, below)
1   turnip, peeled and cut into thick wedges
1   eggplant (aubergine), halved
1   small butternut squash, peeled and cut into large chunks
1   yuca (cassava), 4–5 inches (10–12 cm) long, peeled and cut into large chunks
2   carrots, peeled and cut into large chunks
¼   pound whole okra, trimmed
2   whole *diaxatou* (bitter eggplants), optional
1   handful tamarind pods, pulp only, or 1 tablespoon tamarind paste
2   cups broken white rice (or basmati), rinsed and drained
     salt and freshly ground black pepper
2   limes, cut into wedges, to serve (optional)

     Note: If you can't find *guedj* or *yeet* substitute Vietnamese or Thai fish sauce, about a total of ¼ to ½ cup or less, to taste.

Instructions:

1)   Cut 2 × 2-inch- (5 × 5-cm-) long slits into each fish steak and stuff with about 1 teaspoon of *rof*. Coat the fish with the remaining mixture. Set aside.

2)   Heat the vegetable oil in a large pot over medium-high heat. Add 2 pinches of salt, the onion, green pepper, and tomato paste (purée). Reduce the heat to low and stir well. Stirring occasionally to avoid scorching, cook for 10–15 minutes, or until the vegetables are soft and the tomato paste turns a dark orange. Add the water and stir well. The paste will be thin, becoming sauce-like. Return to a boil, turn the heat to low, and simmer for about 30 minutes.

3)   Carefully add the fish steaks, including the head and tail, to the pot along with the cabbage, *bisaap*, Scotch bonnet peppers, and a pinch of black pepper. Cook uncovered for about 30 minutes over medium heat.

4)   Carefully remove the fish from the pot and set aside in a large bowl. Add the *guedj* and *yeet* (or fish sauce) to the pot. Partially cover the pot, leaving the lid ajar, and simmer for 10 minutes. Add the turnip, eggplant (aubergine) halves, butternut squash, yuca (cassava), carrots, okra, and *diaxatou*. Return to a boil and season with salt and pepper. Reduce the heat to low and simmer for another 30 minutes.

5)   Remove the vegetables from the pot and place in a separate large bowl with a couple ladles of broth (known as *ñeex*). Divide the tamarind equally into the fish and vegetable bowls.

6)   Add the rice to the pot and give it a big stir. Bring to a boil and reduce the heat to low. Use a ladle to skim the excess oil from the top and discard. Tightly cover with a lid and cook until the rice is tender, about 30 minutes. The rice should not have much oil on top and the consistency should resemble dirty rice or *jambalaya*.

7)   When the rice is finished, arrange it on a large platter. Scrape the crust (known as *xooñ*) from the bottom of the pot and place in a small bowl to be served on the side. Arrange the fish and vegetables evenly over the rice. Serve with lime wedges if desired.

ROF

Makes about 1 cup

Ingredients:

3   cloves garlic
1   bunch parsley, coarsely chopped
1   white onion, coarsely chopped
3   scallions (spring onions), chopped
1   bouillon cube (optional)
1   tablespoon hot red pepper (chilli) flakes
1   tablespoon freshly ground black pepper

Instructions:

     Purée all of the ingredients in a food processor, or pound in a mortar and pestle by hand until smooth.

264

THE HUMBOVA

When I was growing up in Northern Ireland, I spent a lot of time next door following Auntie Pauline around her kitchen. She was a great cook and loved trying out recipes. When I was 8 or 9 years old, she made a recipe given to her by someone at the hairdresser's – a sort of marshmallow and peppermint meringue cream. Light and fluffy, it was unlike anything I had ever tasted. Unfortunately, the original recipe is now lost.

My mum and I have re-created it from our memories and it is called The Humbova. The Humbova should be made the day before you actually want to eat it. It is built in layers and letting it rest in the fridge overnight enables the flavours to develop. When you take a spoonful, imagine you are quarrying for clay to make bricks, or are an archaeologist surveying the geological layers of a landscape; every scoop should have a little bit of each strata in it.

Please note: PPE is required for this recipe as humbugs are hard. So aside from your normal baking equipment you will also need a pair of safety goggles and a hammer.

–>

Laura Wilson,
Deepening, 2020.
Still from video,
15:36 minutes.
Commissioned by
New Geographies
and Norwich
Castle Museum
& Art Gallery

Laura Wilson,
The Humbova, 2020

THE HUMBOVA
Serves 6

4 eggs
pinch of salt
250 g caster (superfine) sugar
2 teaspoons cornflour (cornstarch)
1 teaspoon white wine vinegar
600 ml double (heavy) cream
100 g peppermint humbugs (hard black-
  and-white striped peppermint candies)

- First make the meringue. Preheat the oven to 180°C (350°F). Line two baking sheets with baking (parchment) paper.
- Separate the egg whites from the yolks* then whisk the egg whites in a large, clean mixing bowl with a pinch of salt until they form peaks.
- Whisk the sugar, one third at a time, into the egg whites until the whites are stiff and slightly pearlescent. Gently fold in the cornflour (cornstarch) followed by the vinegar.
- Divide the mixture between the two prepared baking sheets using a large spoon to form two circles around 20 cm (8 inches) in diameter. Transfer to the oven, close the door, reduce the heat to 150°C (300°F) and cook for 1¼ hours. Turn off the oven and leave the meringues inside to cool completely – do not open the oven door.
- Meanwhile, pour the cream into a mixing bowl and whip until firm. Put half of the whipped cream into a bowl and place in the refrigerator. Set the other half aside in a separate bowl; keep to hand.
- Place a chopping (cutting) board on a stable work surface (such as a solid work bench or on the ground outdoors), put the humbugs inside a sealed plastic bag and, wearing safety goggles, hammer the humbugs into very fine pieces (almost a dust).

Working quickly, mix most of the smashed humbugs into the whipped cream (reserve a bit of the humbug dust to scatter over the top), cover it with cling film (plastic wrap) and transfer to the refrigerator.
- When the meringues have cooled, make a sandwich with the two meringue circles (imagining they are the bread slices), put the humbug-flavoured cream between them, then top with the plain whipped cream. Scatter the reserved humbug dust over the top.
- Cover with cling film and place in the refrigerator overnight so that the layers have time to settle.
- Serve one generous slice per person.

* Do not waste the remainder of the egg! Use the nutrient-rich egg yolks to make a rich carbonara sauce for pasta and add the eggshells to your next bone stock (broth), or use them in the garden to keep the slugs away from your lettuces.

Laura Wilson,
The Humbova, 2020

Pizha is a popular dish in my hometown that I have loved since my childhood. No matter whether it is for special occasions, weddings or funerals, people will always serve steamed *pizha* or stewed *pizha*, so this dish is very special. I am in my fifties now and whenever I enjoy '*pizha* with meat', the most ancient legacy of the Chinese Shang Dynasty springs to mind. I believe *pizha* originated from the Shang Dynasty; the Emperor of Shang would have had *pizha* when he marched to war. I would like to share this local specialty that has 3,000 years of history, with my friends all over the world.
– Zhang Huan

Pizha is mainly made of sweet potato vermicelli, sweet potato starch, dried small shrimp and seasonings, which are processed through soaking, mixing, steaming, etc. There are many ways to cook *pizha*. It can be fried, stewed, stir-fried and used in soups. Pan-fried *pizha* is the most representative, but *pizha* with dipping sauce and stewed *pizha* are also delicious with their unique flavour. These three are my favourites.

Pan-Fried *Pizha*
-

Cut some *pizha* into 3–5-cm (1¼–2-inch) pieces, chop some spring onions (scallions) and some garlic and set aside. Heat some salad oil in a wok or frying pan (skillet). *Pizha* absorbs a lot of oil, so use 50 per cent more oil than the usual amount. Add the spring onions, then the *pizha* and stir-fry together. Add a moderate amount of salt (based on the amount of salt added when the *pizha* was originally steamed) and a little soy sauce, then add the chopped garlic before serving.

Pizha with Dipping Sauce
-

Cut the *pizha* into 3–5-cm (1¼–2-inch) pieces and serve with a dipping sauce made with soy sauce, vinegar, garlic, chopped spring onions (scallions) and chillies.

Stewed *Pizha*
-

Fry some braised pork belly in a wok or frying pan (skillet), add some soup-stock, and then add the *pizha* to the stew and simmer until it becomes translucent. Add some chopped vegetables, such as courgettes (zucchini), some garlic sprouts, bean sprouts, chopped tofu (bean curd) and other quick and easy things, and cook over a high heat for 2–3 minutes before serving.

Top: *Founding Ceremony of PRC*, 2020, Ash on Linen 160 x 250 cm (63 x 98¼ inches)

ABOUT THE ARTISTS

A CONSTRUCTED WORLD

-

Paris-based artists A Constructed World have produced an extensive body of work over the past twenty-six years. Recent subject matter interrogates who is speaking, and what can and cannot be said. Their performances, activated by people, paintings, objects, speech, conversation, philosophical texts, and music, attempt to counteract the narrowing discourses and tedious processes that pervade the space of culture and politics.

ADEL ABDESSEMED

-

A French artist of Berber origin, Abdessemed was born in Constantine, Algeria in 1971. He lives and works in Paris. Abdessemed held his first solo exhibition in 2001. Since then, other exhibitions have followed, including at MoMA PS1 in New York, and a major retrospective at the Centre Pompidou in Paris. The artist is also represented in public collections, such as Fondation Louis Vuitton in Paris; Moderna Museet in Stockholm; and MAMCO in Geneva.

GHADA AMER

-

Amer's practice spans painting, cast sculpture, ceramics, works on paper, and mixed-media installations, and explores the complicated nature of identity as it is shaped by cultural and religious norms. Her work recognizes that women are taught to model behaviors and traits shaped by others, and that art history (painting, in particular) is largely shaped by expressions of masculinity. Amer's work subverts the masculine/feminine framework. Amer often collaborates with longtime friend Reza Farkhondeh.

EL ANATSUI

-

The Ghanaian sculptor has spent much of his career in Nigeria. He uses typically discarded objects such as bottle caps and cassava graters to create sculpture that defies categorization. His use of these materials reflects his interest in reuse and transformation, and a desire to connect to his continent while transcending the limitations of place. His work interrogates the history of colonialism and draws connections between consumption, waste, and the environment.

ATHANASIOS ARGIANAS

-

Argianas is an interdisciplinary artist working in Athens and London. Argianas and Rowena Hughes run the Daedalus Street project from their studio in Athens, through which they invite artists to produce new performances, in-situ installations, concerts, and publications. Argianas releases music under his own name, or under the alias of his mother's maiden name, Gavouna, on London's Lo Recordings label.

ARTEMIO

-

Artemio is the Rolls Royce of Mexican art.

DAVIDE BALLIANO

-

Balliano originally trained in photography, and his work operates on the thin line that demarcates painting and sculpture. His practice is self-described as monastic, austere, and concrete, and incorporates a strong dialog with architecture. Through his work, he investigates existential themes such as the identity of man in the age of technology, and man's relationship with the sublime.

PIERRE BISMUTH

-

Paris-born Bismuth lives and works in Brussels. His multimedia artworks are collaborative and conceptual in nature, across painting, collage, sculpture, video, film, and performance. He has exhibited widely in Europe. He is preparing a solo show at the Centre Pompidou, where he is planning to install a small chocolate factory to produce Pierre Bismuth's bars to give out to the public.

KATHRIN BÖHM

-

Böhm works in and outside of the art world. Her motto is to think things into being, and her emphasis is on translating ideas for a better future into real life. Her main interests are the collective (re-)production of public space, trade as public realm, and the everyday as a starting point for culture.

OLAF BREUNING

-

Born in Schaffhausen, Switzerland, Breuning originally trained as a photographer. His work encompasses photography, film, drawing, and sculpture, and his works have been exhibited widely in the US and Europe. Breuning lives and works in Upstate New York.

AA BRONSON

-

Vancouver-based AA Bronson founded the artists' group General Idea with Felix Partz and Jorge Zontal in 1969. For twenty-five years, they lived and worked together, exhibiting internationally, inventing new territories for themselves: performance art, video art, queer art, AIDS art. Since Felix and Jorge died of AIDS-related illness in 1994, AA has exhibited as a solo artist, often collaborating with younger generations.

MIRCEA CANTOR

-

Mircea Cantor seeks to address the uncertainty and complexity of life with simple gestures. He works across media as diverse as photography, sculpture, video, drawing, and installation. He was awarded the Prix Marcel Duchamp in 2011, and the Aspen Leadership Prize in 2017 in Romania, and in 2019 was a guest artist at Opéra Nationale de Paris on the occasion of its 350th Anniversary.

SUEJIN CHUNG

-

Born in Seoul, Chung studied Painting at the College of Fine Arts, Hongik University, Seoul, and at School of the Art Institute of Chicago. Chung works and lives in New York.

CLAUDIA COMTE

-

Underpinning Comte's work is her interest in materials. Her practice is guided by a distinct rule-measurement system of her own creation, whereby each artwork relates to one another. Her minimalist approach is methodical yet dynamic, and her work is infused with a sense of playfulness. Comte works in a range of media, but she is best known for her site-specific installations.

COOKING SECTIONS

-

Cooking Sections (Daniel Fernández Pascual and Alon Schwabe) is a duo of spatial practitioners established in 2013. They explore the systems that organise the world through food. Their long-term project CLIMAVORE questions how we eat in the climate emergency. They have exhibited at Tate Britain, the 58th Venice Art Biennale, SALT Istanbul, and Manifesta 12 Palermo among others.

ABRAHAM CRUZVILLEGAS

Cruzvillegas is an active member of the Intergalactic Taoist Tai Chi Society. He is professor at the École Nationale Supérieure des Beaux Arts in Paris.

KEREN CYTTER

-

Cytter creates films, performances, drawings, and photographs. Her work is concerned with topics such as social alienation, language representation, and the function of individuals in predetermined cultural systems. She conducts her practice through experimental modes of storytelling that challenge human perception.

DAWN DEDEAUX AND LONNIE HOLLEY

-

Holley's first artworks were tombstones he carved for his niece and nephew, who died in a house fire. He has never stopped making art out of whatever materials are available. DeDeaux's works from the past fifteen years are influenced by cataclysmic events. She has been envisioning post-Anthropocene life in her MotherShip series, which has featured selections with Holley. The pair have been cooking up "outta space gumbos" since then.

JIMMIE DURHAM

-

The American-born artist, poet, and writer lives in Europe. A 2017 retrospective of his work dating back to the 1970s was shown in the Hammer Museum in Los Angeles, the Walker Art Center in Minneapolis, the Whitney Museum of American Art in New York, and the Remai Modern in Saskatoon, Canada. In 2019, Durham was awarded The Golden Lion for Lifetime Achievement at the 58th International Art Exhibition of La Biennale di Venezia.

STUDIO OLAFUR ELIASSON

-

Olafur Eliasson's work spans sculpture, painting, photography, film, and installation. He strives to engage society at large through art projects and policy-making. Studio Olafur Eliasson, founded in Berlin in 1995, is a team of craftsmen, architects, cooks, and art historians. Since 2005, SOE Kitchen has provided healthy vegetarian food and social glue for the studio team, guests, and visiting collaborators, and is now a platform for exchange among chefs and food activists. *Studio Olafur Eliasson: The Kitchen* was published by Phaidon in 2016.

KLODIN ERB

-

Erb ranks among the best-known Swiss painters. Aware of the rich history of painting, she playfully uses quotations in her expressive, fantastic visual worlds, often questioning definitions of gender and identity. She lives and works in Zurich and is a lecturer at the Department of Design and Art at the University of Lucerne. Her works are represented in numerous public and private collections worldwide and are regularly exhibited in museums.

FALLEN FRUIT

-

Los Angeles-based duo Fallen Fruit is an art collaboration originally conceived in 2004 by David Burns, Matias Viegener, and Austin Young. Since 2013, David and Austin have continued the collaborative work. The duo explore participatory art practice, reflecting upon a global environmental movement involving contemporary art and public spaces. They use everyday objects as material, and have discovered that familiar objects are inextricably bound to identity, and a means for cultural rediscovery.

CHARLES GAINES

-

A pivotal figure in the field of conceptual art, Gaines's work engages formulas and systems that interrogate relationships between the objective and subjective realms. Using a generative approach to create works in a variety of mediums, he has built a bridge between the early conceptual artists of the 1960s and 1970s and subsequent generations. Gaines has had numerous exhibitions, including at The Studio Museum, Harlem and Hammer Museum, Los Angeles, and in 2019 he received the 60th Edward MacDowell Medal.

MEGHAN GORDON AND ARDEN SURDAM

-

Studio Cooking began in 2014 with a question: how do artists feed themselves while they are working (in the studio)? To better understand that artistic division of labor within the context of community-building, privacy, gender, and the politics of hosting, co-founders Meghan Gordon and Arden Surdam commissioned meals, edible artworks, food-adjacent performances, recipes and lectures. Based in Los Angeles, Surdam is an artist working in photography and sculpture, and Gordon is an artist, writer, and gallery director contemplating the intersections of labor, language, and pleasure.

SUBODH GUPTA

-

Gupta is one of India's most renowned contemporary artists. He is known for transforming everyday objects into installations that engage with his childhood, his home country, and universal themes like migration, globalization, and the cosmos. His installations often comprise objects, such as utensils, that evoke either the exotic or the quotidian, depending on the viewer's perspective.

JOÃO MARIA GUSMÃO

-

Lisbon-based Gusmão, working with Pedro Paiva, has developed a complex artistic practice that incorporates experimental film, sculpture, photography, literature, curating, and publishing. The duo's work mostly takes the form of experimental 16-mm film footage in which references of modern/postmodern literature and imagery overlap with contemporary philosophy.

NIKOLAI HAAS

-

Haas is one half of the art duo The Haas Brothers. Born in Austin, Texas, he now resides in Los Angeles with his wife and young son. He practices art professionally with his twin brother Simon Haas.

LYLE ASHTON HARRIS

-

Harris has cultivated a diverse artistic practice, ranging from photography and collage to installation and performance art. His work explores intersections between the personal and the political, examining the ways in which ethnicity, gender, and desire impact on contemporary social and cultural life.

JEPPE HEIN

-

Hein is known for experiential, interactive artworks that meet where art, architecture, and technical inventions intersect. His works engage in a lively dialog with the traditions of Minimalist sculpture and 1970s' conceptual art. The element of surprise often figures in his work, placing viewers at the center of events and focusing on their experience and perception of the space.

GREGOR HILDEBRANDT

-

Berlin-based Hildebrandt works mainly with analog sound storage mediums. Using molded vinyl records, audio tapes, and cassette tape casings, he creates sculptures, installations, and paintings that typically reference sound, adding a further layer of dimension to his minimalist works. He has been Professor of Painting and Prints at the Academy of Fine Arts in Munich since 2015.

CARSTEN HÖLLER

-

Höller uses his training as a scientist in his work as an artist, concentrating on the nature of human relationships. Born in Brussels in 1961, he now lives and works in Stockholm, Sweden, and Biriwa, Ghana. He has had major installations and solo exhibitions in London, New York, Milan, Mexico City, Vienna, and beyond.

CHRISTIAN HOLSTAD

-

Holstad's work probes preconceptions about class, culture, sexuality, and society, examining high and low culture. His work encompasses sculpture, installation, performance, photography, collage, and textiles. He has an interest in consumer culture, and his work investigates the borders, boundaries, and constraints that impact on our lives, from the political and governmental to the societal and personal.

DAVID HORVITZ

-

The artist's work considers strategies of information circulation and the impermanence of digital artifacts. Poetically playful, Horvitz meddles with the systems of language, time, and networks, and the measuring and recording of distances. His practice encompasses language, photography, performance, ephemera, books, food, sound, watercolor, and mail.

DOROTHY IANNONE

-

Now part of the permanent collections of the Centre Pompidou, Tate Modern, Berlinische Galerie, and Migros Museum, Iannone has exhibited widely internationally. Recent solo exhibitions include Remai Modern, Saskatoon, Canada (2019) and Centre Pompidou, Paris (2019).

EMILY JACIR

-

An artist and filmmaker, Jacir is primarily concerned with transformation, translation, and resistance, and of silenced historical narratives. Her work investigates personal and collective movement through public space, and the physical and social implications that result. She has built up a compelling oeuvre across a range of media, using methodologies based on in-depth research into historical material.

JOHANNA JACKSON AND CHRIS JOHANSON

-

Jackson and Johanson are artists based in Oregon and California. They make art sometimes together, sometimes individually. Their creativity is expressed in a variety of media, including painting, sculpture, music, and cookery although their favorite art is enjoying/enduring life.

RAGNAR KJARTANSSON

-

The history of film, music, theatre, visual culture, and literature find their way into Kjartansson's video installations and performances, and feature in his drawing and painting too. Pretending and staging are key tools in the artist's attempt to convey sincerity of emotion, and to offer a genuine experience to his audience.

ALICJA KWADE

Through her work, Kwade investigates and questions societal structures, and reflects on the perceptual habits that inform everyday life. Her diverse practice encompasses sculpture, video, photography, and public installations, and is based around concepts of space, time, science, and philosophy. Her works belong to several international private and public collections.

JULIO LE PARC

-

Le Parc is a major figure of historical importance within kinetic and contemporary art. His early paintings were influenced by the Constructivist movement known as Arte Concreto Invención and by artists such as Piet Mondrian. Since 1959, he has forged his own path, applying rigorous organizing principles to his paintings. His research into perceptual instability as a pioneer of kinetic and Op Art led to important works involving light and movement.

NATALIA LL

-

Wrocław-based Natalia Lach-Lachowicz is an artist working in several forms of media, including photography, video, painting, installation, drawing, and performance. She was a senior lecturer at the Fine Arts Academy in Poznań from 2004–20. Since 1971 she has been active under the name "Natalia LL." Her works are often classified as conceptual art, photo art, or body art.

JOHN LYONS

Lyons moved to the UK from Trinidad and Tobago in the late 1950s to study art. A prize-winning poet and established painter, he has contributed to numerous anthologies, and has published six collections of his own poetry. His seventh, "Cook-up in a Trini Kitchen," contains poems about food and recipes, illustrated with John's own watercolors and pen drawings. He is dedicated to promoting the arts through community workshops, teaching, and public performances.

ANNA MARIA MAIOLINO

-

Maiolino's art is concerned with creative and destructive processes. Working across drawing, printmaking, poetry, film, performance, installation, and sculpture, she explores notions of subjectivity and self. Her early experiments in the 1960s connected the artist to important movements in Brazilian art. Since the early 1980s Maiolino has worked with malleable materials that, through her handling, come to bear the imprint of unconscious gestures and life's daily rituals.

HAROON MIRZA

-

London-born Mirza has a BA in Painting from Winchester School of Art, an MA in Design Critical Practice and Theory from Goldsmiths College (2006), and an MA in Fine Art from Chelsea College of Art and Design (2007). Recent solo exhibitions have been held at CCA Kitakyushu, Kitakyushu, Japan (2020); Haüsler Contemporary, Zurich (2019); and Australian Centre for Contemporary Art, Melbourne, Australia (2019).

MICHAEL MORRIS

-

Known as an abstract painter, Morris has worked in film, video, photography, installation, and performance. A catalyst in the Vancouver art scene of the 1960s and 70s, he is known for his collaborative artistic practice, and his ability to shift between roles of artist, curator, arts administrator, and cultural player. In 1973, Morris and seven colleagues founded Western Front Society for the production and presentation of "New Art," which still thrives.

VIK MUNIZ

-

Muniz's signature style appropriates and reinterprets iconic contemporary images. His works have been shown at the Museum of Modern Art in New York, Tate Modern in London, and Museu de Arte Moderna in São Paulo. "Waste Land," a documentary about his work in Rio de Janeiro's favelas, was nominated for an Academy Award in 2010. Muniz is involved in several educational, social, and humanitarian projects in Brazil and the US.

EAMON ORE-GIRON

American artist Ore-Giron blends a wide range of visual styles and influences in his brightly colored, abstract geometric paintings. Referencing indigenous and craft traditions such as Native American medicine wheels and Amazonian tapestries, as well as twentieth-century Western avant-garde art movements, his paintings resonate across cultural contexts. Ore-Giron also works in video and music. His interdisciplinary projects explore the interrelationship of sound, color, rhythm, and pattern.

ZAK OVÉ

-

Ové is a London-born multi-disciplinary artist who works across sculpture, film, and photography. His work is informed by the history and lore carried through the African diaspora to the Caribbean, Britain, and beyond, with particular focus on traditions of masking and masquerade as tools of self-emancipation. Ové seeks to unveil the invisible and to re-write a history for the future through heralding the past in a new light.

ADRIAN PACI

-

Albania-born Paci studied painting at the Academy of Art of Tirana before moving to Milan in 1997, where he now lives and works. He has held a number of solo shows, most recently at Kunsthalle Krems (2019), Austria, and Museo Novecento, Florence (2017). His work has all been part of group shows, including the 14th International Architecture Exhibition, La Biennale di Venezia in 2014.

PHILIPPE PARRENO

-

As an artist, Parreno seeks to redefine the exhibition experience by treating it as a medium, placing its construction at the heart of the artistic process. Working in film, sculpture, drawing, and text, Parreno conceives his exhibitions as a scripted space where a series of events unfold. He has exhibited at the Tate Modern and The Serpentine Gallery in London, Palais de Tokyo in Paris, and the Museum of Modern Art in New York.

NICOLAS PARTY

-

Party is both a figurative painter, and a creator of public murals, sculpture, and installations. His unsettling landscapes, portraits, and still-life paintings celebrate and challenge conventions of representational works. Created in soft pastel, they allow for exceptional degrees of intensity and fluidity in his depictions of natural and manmade objects. Transforming these objects into abstracted, biomorphic shapes, Party suggests deeper connections and meanings.

LUIZA PRADO DE O. MARTINS

-

Prado de O. Martins is an artist, writer, and researcher whose work examines themes around reproduction, herbal medicine, coloniality, gender, and race. She is part of the curatorial board of transmediale 2021 and an assistant professor and vice-director of the Centre for Other Worlds at the Lusófona University in Lisbon. She is a founding member of Decolonising Design.

LAURE PROUVOST

-

Prouvost divides her working life between Monaco and Knokke in Belgium. Her multifaceted practice involves everything from creating soundscapes and installations, to making objects as diverse as boobs and teacups. Prouvost has exhibited widely, from Venice and Milan, to Minneapolis and Brussels.

MICHAEL RAKOWITZ

-

Rakowitz is an artist living and working in Chicago. His work has appeared in venues the world over, including documenta (13), Palais de Tokyo, and CURRENT:LA Public Art Triennial. He is the recipient of numerous prizes, including the 2020 Nasher Sculpture Prize and the 2018 Herb Alpert Award in Visual Arts and was awarded the Fourth Plinth commission (2018–2020) in London's Trafalgar Square. From 2019 to 2020, a survey of his work traveled from Whitechapel Gallery in London, to Castello di Rivoli Museo d'Arte Contemporanea in Turin, to the Jameel Arts Centre in Dubai.

ASAD RAZA

-

In his work, Asad Raza seeks to reject traditional disciplinary boundaries, and to combine the experiences of beings (human and non-human) and their interaction with objects. He conceives of art as a metabolic, active experience, as something in which visitors and viewers can engage in playful exchanges of meaning.

TOBIAS REHBERGER

-

Rehberger is one of the most influential, successful German artists of his generation. The concept of transformation is a central theme of his art. Working in a variety of forms including sculpture, industrial objects, and handcrafted articles, he explores structural design and architecture. His work thrives on chance connections and unexpected encounters. The themes of perception and awareness, temporality and transience, and of discontinuity and ambiguity inform his work.

ANTONIO RIELLO

-

Before becoming an artist, Riello studied pharmaceutical chemistry at Padua University. He is fascinated by the paradoxes and controversies of contemporary Western life. Much of his work is concerned with the ambiguity and subversive manipulation of social and cultural life.

MARTHA ROSLER

-

Brooklyn-based Rosler works in video, photography, text, installation, and performance. Her work addresses the landscapes of everyday life—actual and virtual—especially as they affect women. She has long produced works on war and the national security climate, connecting life at home with the conduct of war abroad, and has published several books of photographs, texts, and commentary on public space. In 2010 she received the Guggenheim Museum Lifetime Achievement Award.

MARK SADLER

-

A painter, writer, and musician, Sadler lives in Glasgow and Berlin. After graduating from Glasgow School of Art in 1990, he hitchhiked through Europe to Syria, then spent long periods in India and Pakistan, and three years in Paris. In 1997 he and fellow artist Elín Jakobsdóttir founded Fiction House in Berlin, which hosts discussions, puppet performances, music, and exhibitions.

ZINA SARO-WIWA

-

Through her art, British-Nigerian Saro-Wiwa seeks to transform people's understanding of environmentalism. For her, this implicates not just worries about greenhouse emissions and oil pollution, but also emotional landscapes, spiritual ecosystems, traditional art, indigenous epistemologies, food, and drink. She uses video art, film and documentary-making, writing, curatorial projects, and food initiatives to construct an integrated thesis about the ways in which humanity inhabits earth's realms.

SHIMABUKU

-

In 2017 Shimabuku moved from Berlin, where he had lived for twelve years, to Naha, Japan. He works in a diverse range of media including sculpture, film, and photography. His style has gained a worldwide reputation for being full of poetic sentiment and humor. Since the 1990s, he has traveled widely, creating performances and installations that consider the daily lives and cultures of people he encounters.

TIFFANY SIA

-

Hong Kong-born Sia is an artist, filmmaker, and founder of Speculative Place. She is the author of 咸濕 *Salty Wet* (Inpatient Press, 2019). Sia is the director of the short, experimental film Never Rest/Unrest, which screened at the Museum of Modern Art's Doc Fortnight and at Berwick Film & Media Arts Festival. Sia's first institutional exhibition, "Slippery When Wet," was at Artists Space, New York and centered on her book 更咸更濕 *Too Salty Too Wet* (Speculative Place Press, 2021).

KIKI SMITH

-

Smith explores mortality, regeneration and gender politics, observing the interconnection of spirituality and the natural world through a postmodern lens. Her work embraces glassmaking, printmaking, watercolor, photography, and textiles, and is inspired by the visual culture of the past, from Byzantine iconography and medieval altarpieces to eighteenth-century anatomical drawings.

NEDKO SOLAKOV

-

Since the early 1990s Solakov has exhibited extensively in Europe and the US. His works belong to more than fifty international museums and public collections, among them the Museum of Modern Art in New York, Tate Modern in London, and the Centre Pompidou in Paris.

CALLY SPOONER

-

The London-based artist's diverse practice includes multimedia installations, novels, radio broadcasts, plays, music, and performances. Solo presentations of her work have been held throughout Europe, in the UK, and in the US. Her books include the collection *Scripts* (SlimVolume, 2016) and the novel, *Collapsing in Parts* (Mousse, 2013).

JAIME SUNWOO

-

Sunwoo is a Korean-American multidisciplinary artist from Brooklyn, New York. Her works connect personal narratives to global histories through surreal storytelling. She studied art at Yale University, and was a fellow for Ping Chong and Company and The Laundromat Project. Her project Specially Processed American Me has received awards from Queens Council on the Arts, Asian Women Giving Circle, NYC Women's Fund, Brooklyn Arts Fund, and The Jim Henson Foundation.

RIRKRIT TIRAVANIJA

-

The Argentinian-born, Thai artist is known for overturning traditional exhibition formats in favor of social interactions through the sharing of everyday activities such as cooking, and reading. Creating environments that reject the primacy of the art object, and instead focus on use value and the bringing of people together through communal care, Tiravanija's work challenges expectations around labor and virtuosity. He is on the faculty of the School of the Arts at Columbia University, and helped establish The Land Foundation, an educational-ecological project in Thailand.

CAIQUE TIZZI

-

Tizzi is an artist, cook, and event organizer. The focus of his practice revolves around an artistic approach to food, in which the kitchen becomes part studio, part laboratory. His culinary experiences aim to create a ritual around the table, giving an aura of theatricality to the ordinary, mundane act of eating together. In 2011, Tizzi co-founded Agora Collective in Berlin and developed its artistic and food platforms until 2019.

VINCENT TRASOV

-

Trasov is a painter and video and performance artist whose work is often media-based and collaborative in spirit. In 1969 he and fellow artist Michael Morris founded Image Bank, a means for information exchange among artists. In 1973, he and Morris co-founded Western Front Society in Vancouver, for the production and presentation of "New Art." Trasov has had numerous international exhibitions and resides in Germany and Canada.

BERNAR VENET

-

Venet uses pure science as a subject for his art in a career spanning painting, poetry, sculpture, film, and performance, from the 1960s to the present day. The recipient of France's *Chevalier de la Légion d'honneur*, his work is exhibited in more than 70 museums worldwide. The Venet Foundation aims to preserve the site of the artist's home in France to ensure the artist's work lives on after him.

DANH VO

-

The Vo family escaped Vietnam to Denmark in 1979, and the artist's work embodies the shifting, precarious nature of contemporary life. Vo imagines a world for the artist unbound by obligations to state institutions, social norms, and grand humanist projects. His work is a series of experiments, questioning what happens if he brings various sets of elements together. Power, history, eroticism, personal biography, imperial dissolution, and globalist expansion all come into play.

KEHINDE WILEY

-

Wiley is best known for his portraits that render people of color in the traditional settings of Old Master paintings. His work brings art history face-to-face with contemporary culture, using the visual rhetoric of the heroic, the powerful, the majestic, and the sublime to celebrate Black and Brown people. Wiley's paintings, sculpture, and video challenge and reorient art-historical narratives, awakening complex issues that many would prefer remain muted.

LAURA WILSON

-

London-based Wilson is interested in how history and embodied knowledge is carried and evolved through everyday materials, trades, and craftsmanship. She works with specialists to develop sculptural and performative works that amplify the relationship between materiality, memory, and tacit knowledge. A Fellow of the Winston Churchill Memorial Trust, Wilson has been awarded the inaugural Jerwood New Work Fund and the Dover Prize 2021.

ZHANG HUAN

-

The first contemporary Chinese artist, Zhang held a large-scale solo exhibition, "In the Ashes of History" in Russia in 2020 and achieved unprecedented success. Zhang's artworks are widely collected by museums and private and public collections. In 2014 he was awarded the *Chevalier de la Légion d'honneur* by the French government in recognition of his contribution to the communication of Chinese culture.

INDEX

Page numbers in *italics* refer to the recipe images.

RECIPE NOTES

All butter is salted unless otherwise specified.

-

All sugar is superfine (caster) sugar, unless otherwise specified.

-

All milk is whole (full-fat), unless otherwise specified.

-

All eggs are US large (UK medium), unless otherwise specified.

-

Individual vegetables and fruits, such as carrots and apples, are assumed to be medium, unless otherwise specified.

-

Some of the recipes require advanced techniques, specialist equipment, and professional experience to achieve good results.

-

Exercise a high level of caution when following recipes involving any potentially hazardous activity, including the use of high temperatures, open flames, and when deep-frying. In particular, when deep-frying add food carefully to avoid splashing, wear long sleeves and never leave the pan unattended.

-

Cooking times are for guidance only. If using a fan (convection) oven, follow the manufacturer's instructions concerning the oven temperatures.

-

Some recipes include lightly cooked eggs, meat, and fish and fermented products. These should be avoided by the elderly, infants, pregnant women, convalescents, and anyone with an impaired immune system.

Exercise caution when making fermented products, ensuring all equipment is spotlessly clean, and seek expert advice if in any doubt.

-

Exercise caution and wear protective clothing when undertaking any butchering work.

-

All herbs, shoots, flowers, berries, seeds, and vegetables should be picked fresh from a clean source. Exercise caution when foraging for ingredients. Any foraged ingredients should only be eaten if an expert has deemed them safe to eat.

-

When no quantity is specified, for example of oils, salts, and herbs used for finishing dishes, quantities are discretionary and flexible.

-

All spoon and cup measurements are level, unless otherwise stated. 1 teaspoon = 5 ml; 1 tablespoon = 15 ml. Australian standard tablespoons are 20 ml, so Australian readers are advised to use 3 teaspoons in place of 1 tablespoon when measuring small quantities.

RECIPE NOTES

The publishers would like to thank:
–

Maria Thereza Alves, Hamid Amini, Matt Arnett, Nick Ash, Pia Austin-Little, Chanez Baali, Stephan Babendererde, Lutz Bantel, Erika Benincasa, Pierre Bismuth, Marianne Boesky, Alberto Bremermann, Maria-Thalia Carras, Aaron Cezar, Jennifer Chert, Jisoo Chung, Yeon Shim Chung, Toby Clarke, Billie S. Clarken, Pilar Corrias, Maisey Cox, Philippe Da Silva, Ella De Cleyn, Stefan Düe, Susan Dunne, Olivia Fairweather, Vanessa Fuentes, Maudie Gibbons, Massimiliano Gioni, Patrick Gosatti, Lilja Gunnarsdóttir, Haru Heshiki, Isabelle Hogenkamp, Rowena Hughes, Evan Jorgensen, Peter Kaiser, Stella Karafili, Nicole Keller, Kristina Köper, Sabina Kohler, Marie Krauss, Silvana Lagos, Inga Liesenfeld, Nada Lottermann, Florian Lüdde, Marta Lusena, Jacki Mansfield, Monica Manzutto, Róisín McQueirns, Aleksandra Mir, Mary Mitsch, Audrey Moyer, Ananya Mukhopadhyay, Peter Nagy, Slava Nakovska, Rachel Nawi, Camila Nichols, Michel Nikodem, David Norr, Amarachi Okafor, Audrey Pédron, Alberto Peola, Wiebke Petersen, Raphaëlle Pinoncély, Nicolas Polli, Mona Pouillon, Josh Rabineau, David Raccuglia, Agnieszka Rayzacher, Asad Raza, Jean Rees-Lyons, Margery Reich, Alina Rentsch, Angela Rodel, Jane M. Saks, Kathryn Sawabini, Emelia Scheidt, Karin Seinsoth, Rosey Selig-Addiss, Joshua Selman, Adam Sheffer, Chloe Sideris, Vincent Simon, Dimitar Solakov, María Sprowls Cervantes, Evan Sung, Aideé Tapia Guzman, Clarissa Tempestini, Clara Ustinov, Tiffany Wang, Gary Waterston, Christina Werner, Courtney Willis Blair, Maggie Ying, and Michaela Züge-Bruton.

Special thanks also go to the following institutions:
–

Air de Paris, Paris; Marianne Boesky Gallery, New York; ChertLüdde, Berlin; James Cohan, New York; Pilar Corrias Gallery, London; Delfina Foundation, London; Hauser & Wirth, Zurich, New York, and Los Angeles; KuriManzutto, Mexico City; Lokal_30, Warsaw; Mitchell-Innes & Nash, New York; Nature Morte, New Delhi; Pace, New York; Peola Simondi, Turin; and Perrotin, Paris.

Phaidon Press Limited
2 Cooperage Yard
London
E15 2QR

Phaidon Press Inc.
65 Bleecker Street
New York, NY 10012

phaidon.com

First published 2021
© 2021 Phaidon Press Limited

ISBN 978 1 83866 331 5

Commissioning Editors: Michele Robecchi and Emilia Terragni
Project Editor: Sophie Hodgkin
Production Controller: Sarah Kramer
Layout: Julia Hasting with Studio Chehade
Design: Julia Hasting

The Publisher would like to thank Susan Low, Elizabeth Parson,
Sally Somers, and Caroline Stearns for their contributions
to the book.

Printed in Italy